NUFFI

SCIENCE

CALCULATIONS

Editor of this book **David Sang**

Authors of this book **David Sang**
         Jean McLean
         Terry Parkin

Contributor   **Andrew Hunt**

The Nuffield Foundation is grateful to Richard Sale and Neill Travers for
checking the material, and to the publishing editor Laurice Suess.

Addison Wesley Longman Limited 1996
Edinburgh Gate, Harlow, Essex CM20 2JE, England and Associated
Companies throughout the world

First published 1996

Illustrations by Hugh Neill
Illustration page 27 by Nathan Barlex
Cartoons by Ralph Hancock

Printed in Singapore

ISBN 0 582 23730 0

NUFFIELD

SCIENCE

CALCULATIONS

Published for the Nuffield-Chelsea Curriculum Trust
by Longman Group Limited

 LONGMAN

CONTENTS

◆ BIOLOGY

◆ ANSWERS

◆ REFERENCE SECTION

INTRODUCTION

Science is one of the subjects in which you make use of what you have learned in Maths. Scientists spend a lot of time recording their measurements, and then doing mathematical calculations to make sense of them.

This book will help you master the calculations involved in your GCSE Science course. It is divided up into a lot of individual topics. Each topic is presented in three parts.

◆ A summary of the ideas you will need to know, including any important formulas. You should already have studied these ideas during your Science lessons.

◆ Worked examples, to show you how to tackle problems in a step-by-step way. These will also show you how to set out your calculations clearly.

◆ Questions to solve. The first questions in each topic are straightforward, but they become gradually more difficult as you work your way through them.

Once you have mastered a particular topic in this book, you should be able to answer any similar questions in GCSE tests and exams.

◆ SCIENTIFIC EQUATIONS

There are several different ways of showing how quantities are related to each other. Here are four different ways of showing the relationship between current, voltage and resistance:

voltage = current × resistance

$V = I \times R$

volts = amperes × ohms

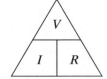

Different people have different ways of remembering relationships like this. The best way is to remember what the quantities mean. If you understand what voltage, current and resistance mean, then you will remember how they are related.

However, you may need to use the relationship before you have a very firm grasp of the ideas. If this is the case, it is a good idea to memorize one form of the equation. It is up to you to decide which one to memorize: if you learn the equation in symbols ($V = IR$), then you must know what the symbols mean. If you learn the units equation, then you must know what they are the units of. Some people prefer to learn the 'equation triangle', because it is more visual.

In this book we have provided many equation triangles. They can help you to rearrange an equation, in order to make a different quantity its subject. Cover up the quantity that you want to make the subject of the equation (the quantity which you want to find).

To find V:

$$V = I \times R$$

To find I:

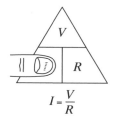

$$I = \frac{V}{R}$$

PHYSICS

MOTION

◆ TOPIC 1 SPEED

The **speed** of a moving object tells us how fast it is moving
– how many metres it travels during each second:

$$\text{speed (m/s)} = \frac{\text{distance (m)}}{\text{time (s)}} \qquad v = \frac{s}{t}$$

$$\text{distance} = \text{speed} \times \text{time} \qquad s = v \times t$$

$$\text{time} = \frac{\text{distance}}{\text{speed}} \qquad t = \frac{s}{v}$$

Don't confuse *s* for distance with s for seconds!

UNITS

The standard units for speed are m/s, with distance in metres and
time in seconds. Other units are possible:

$$\text{speed (km/h)} = \frac{\text{distance (km)}}{\text{time (h)}}$$

It can be useful to remember that 10 mph is approximately 4 m/s
and 10 m/s is approximately 25 mph.

WORKED EXAMPLE 1A

Question

A runner wins a 200 m race in 25.0 s. What is her average speed?

Answer

Step 1   Write down what you know, and $s = 200$ m
what you want to know. $t = 25.0$ s
                                                $v = ?$

Step 2   Use the symbols triangle to choose $v = \dfrac{s}{t}$
the appropriate form of the equation.

Step 3   Substitute in the values and work $v = \dfrac{200\,\text{m}}{25\,\text{s}} = 8\,\text{m/s}$
out the answer.

Her average speed is 8.0 m/s.

Questions

1.1 What is the average speed of a racing car that travels 2000 m round a track in 32 s?

1.2 A dolphin can swim at 12 m/s. How long will it take to swim from end to end of a pool 180 m in length?

1.3 A supersonic aircraft is travelling at 600 m/s. How far will it travel in 30 s?

1.4 Which is the faster, a snail that moves 1 m in 400 s or a slug that moves 0.28 m in 140 s?

1.5 Two sprinters are racing over 200 m. The winner has an average speed of 10 m/s. The loser's average speed is 9 m/s. How long does the winner take? How far has the loser run in this time?

1.6 A student stands near a cliff, fires a gun and hears the echo 1.4 s later. How far is the student from the cliff? (The speed of sound in air is 330 m/s.)

In questions 1.7 to 1.11, you will have to be careful about the units used.

1.7 A train is travelling at 80 mph. How long will it take to cover a distance of 140 miles?

1.8 Concorde travels at 2000 km/h. How far will it fly in $3\frac{1}{2}$ hours?

1.9 A police patrol car recorded a motorist speeding at 90 mph on a road where the speed limit was 60 mph. If the motorist was travelling a distance of 30 miles, how much longer would the journey have taken if she did not break the law? (Give your answer in minutes.)

1.10 A new jet aircraft is timed on a test flight. It covers 30 km in exactly one minute. What is its speed? (Give your answer both in m/s and in km/h.)

1.11 A fish swims round and round its bowl. If the diameter of the bowl is 30 cm and it goes round 15 times in one minute, what is its average speed, in cm/s?

◆ DISTANCE–TIME GRAPHS

The slope (**gradient**) of a distance–time graph tells us the speed of a moving object. The steeper the graph, the greater the speed. A horizontal graph means a speed of 0 m/s: the object is stationary.

The speed is the slope (gradient) of the graph.

You can find the speed of a moving object from its distance–time graph. Worked example 1B shows you how.

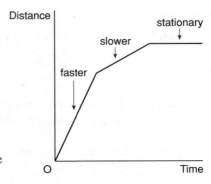

WORKED EXAMPLE 1B

Question

What is the speed of the car whose distance–time graph is shown here?

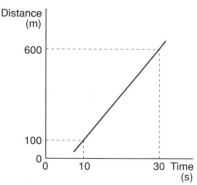

Answer

Step 1   Choose two suitable (well-separated) points on the graph.

Step 2   Work out the distance travelled between the two points, by looking across to the distance axis and finding the difference between the two distances.

$$\text{initial distance} = 100 \text{ m}$$
$$\text{final distance} = 600 \text{ m}$$
$$\text{distance travelled} = 600 \text{ m} - 100 \text{ m} = 500 \text{ m}$$

Step 3   Work out the time interval between the two points, by looking down to the time axis and finding the difference between the two times.

$$\text{initial time} = 10 \text{ s}$$
$$\text{final time} = 30 \text{ s}$$
$$\text{time taken} = 30 \text{ s} - 10 \text{ s} = 20 \text{ s}$$

> If you are familiar with working out the gradient of a graph, you will probably be able to reduce the number of steps in this type of calculation.

Step 4   Work out the speed of the car.

$$\text{speed} = \frac{\text{distance}}{\text{time}} = \frac{500 \text{ m}}{20 \text{ s}} = 25 \text{ m/s}$$

The speed of the car is 25 m/s.

Questions

1.12 This is the distance–time graph for a train. In which section of the journey was it

a travelling fastest?

b stationary?

c travelling most slowly (but not stationary)?

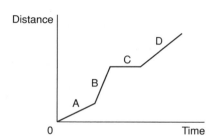

1.13 Which car is travelling the fastest? Which is travelling the slowest?

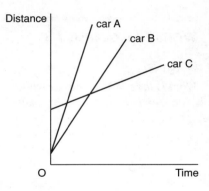

1.14 Sketch a distance–time graph to show this journey:
You are walking slowly to school. You meet a friend and stop for a chat. You set off slowly again; then you realize that you will be late, and run all the rest of the way.

1.15 The graph shows how a racehorse moved when it was out for a training run. What was its speed in sections AB, BC and CD?

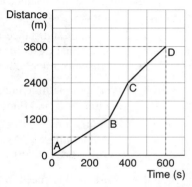

1.16 A driver wanted to check his car's speedometer. He drove along a motorway with the speedometer reading a steady 65 mph. His passenger recorded the time and the distance to London whenever they passed a signpost:

Time (hours : mins)	3:10	3:17	3:24	3:30	3:38
Distance from London (miles)	74	67	60	54	46

Draw a distance–time graph, and use it to find the car's average speed. Is the speedometer reliable?

1.17 A long-distance runner jogs for 15 minutes at 12 km/h. She then speeds up and runs for a further 20 minutes at 15 km/h. Draw an accurate distance–time graph for her run, and use it to work out her average speed over the whole run.

4

TOPIC 2 ACCELERATION

An object is **accelerating** if its speed is changing. Increasing speed is acceleration; decreasing speed is deceleration.

$$\text{acceleration } (\text{m/s}^2) = \frac{\text{change in speed (m/s)}}{\text{time taken (s)}}$$

Or: acceleration $= \dfrac{\text{final speed} - \text{initial speed}}{\text{time taken}}$ $a = \dfrac{v - u}{t}$

Sometimes we know the acceleration, and we want to calculate the speed which this will result in.

final speed = initial speed + (acceleration × time) $v = u + at$

UNITS

The standard units of acceleration are m/s^2. An object has an acceleration of 1 m/s^2 if its speed changes by 1 m/s in 1 s.

WORKED EXAMPLE 2A

Question

A runner has been running at 7 m/s for most of a race. She speeds up to 10 m/s for the last sprint. If it takes her 1.5 s to do this, what is her acceleration?

Answer

Step 1 Write down what you know, and what you want to know.

$u = 7$ m/s
$v = 10$ m/s
$t = 1.5$ s
$a = ?$

Step 2 Choose the appropriate form of the equation.

$a = \dfrac{v - u}{t}$

Step 3 Substitute in the values and work out the answer.

Take care to work out the subtraction first.

$$a = \frac{10\,\text{m/s} - 7\,\text{m/s}}{1.5\,\text{s}} = \frac{3\,\text{m/s}}{1.5\,\text{s}} = 2\,\text{m/s}^2$$

The runner's acceleration is 2 m/s^2.

Questions

2.1 At the start of a race, a sprinter reaches a speed of 10 m/s in 2.5 s. What is his acceleration?

2.2 A stone is dropped down a well. After 1 s, its speed is 10 m/s. After 3 s, its speed is 30 m/s. What is its acceleration?

2.3 A train slows down at an amber signal. Its speed drops from 20 m/s to 8 m/s in 60 s. What is its deceleration?

2.4 A cyclist, travelling at 15 m/s, brakes so that her deceleration is 3 m/s^2. How fast will she be travelling after 3 s? How long will it take her to stop completely?

2.5 Car A speeds up from 30 mph to 60 mph in 8 s. Car B accelerates from a standstill to 50 mph in 12 s. Which has the greater acceleration? (Work out the two accelerations in mph/s.)

2.6 An object dropped on the Moon accelerates downwards at 1.6 m/s^2.
a How fast would a stone be falling after 1 s? ... after 2 s?
b If a stone is thrown upwards with an initial speed of 8 m/s, how fast will it be moving after 1 s? ... after 2 s?

2.7 A plane accelerates along the runway. It takes 7 s to reach a speed of 100 km/h. How long will it take to reach its take-off speed of 300 km/h?

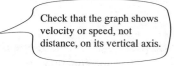

There is a quick way to solve this.

◆ VELOCITY–TIME GRAPHS

The slope (gradient) of a velocity–time graph tells you the acceleration of a moving object.

Check that the graph shows velocity or speed, not distance, on its vertical axis.

◆ Speeding up (accelerating): graph slopes upwards.
◆ Slowing down (decelerating): graph slopes downwards.
◆ Steady speed: graph horizontal.
◆ Stationary: speed = 0.

In this section, velocity has the same meaning as speed. (Strictly speaking, velocity is speed *in a particular direction*.)

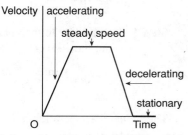

WORKED EXAMPLE 2B

Question

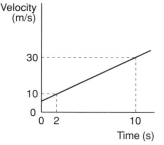

The graph shows how the speed of a car changed as it travelled along a straight road. What was the acceleration of the car?

Answer

Step 1   Select two suitable points on the graph.

Step 2   Work out the change in speed between these two points.

change in speed = $v - u$ = 30 m/s – 10 m/s = 20 m/s

Step 3   Work out the time between these two points.

time taken = 10 s – 2 s = 8 s

Step 4   Work out the acceleration.

$$\text{acceleration} = \frac{\text{change in speed}}{\text{time taken}} = \frac{20\,\text{m/s}}{8\,\text{s}} = 2.5\,\text{m/s}^2$$

The car's acceleration is 2.5 m/s^2.

Questions

2.8 The graph shows the speed of a train along a section of its journey.

   a What is its initial speed?

   b What is its speed after 50 s?

   c What is its acceleration?

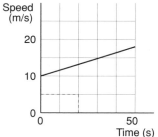

2.9 The graph shows the speed of a bus as it travelled along part of its journey. During which section(s) of the journey was it

   a stationary?

   b accelerating?

   c decelerating?

   d moving fastest?

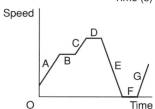

2.10 A racing car under test produced the following figures:

Speed (km/h)	0	80	160	210	260	260	260
Time (s)	0	5	10	15	20	25	30

  a Draw a velocity–time graph for this run.
  b Calculate the car's acceleration (in km/h per second) during the first 10 s.
  c Calculate its acceleration during the next 10 s.
  d What is its acceleration during the last 10 s?

2.11 Sketch a velocity–time graph to show the following journey:
A train starts off from a station and accelerates to a steady speed. It maintains this speed for a while, until it passes an amber signal. The driver then brakes so that it slows down gradually; the next signal is green, so the driver speeds up again.

◆ DISTANCES AND AVERAGE SPEEDS

If an object is accelerating, we can still work out how far it travels in a particular time. We do this by first working out the **average speed**:

$$\text{average speed} = \frac{\text{initial speed} + \text{final speed}}{2} = \frac{v+u}{2}$$

$$\text{distance travelled} = \text{average speed} \times \text{time} = \frac{v+u}{2} \times t$$

Note that the acceleration *must* be steady (uniform); that is, the velocity–time graph must be a straight line.

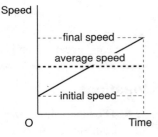

WORKED EXAMPLE 2C

Question

A car accelerates from 4 m/s to 20 m/s in a time of 10 s. How far does it travel in this time?

Answer

  Step 1   Calculate the average speed.

$$\text{average speed} = \frac{v+u}{2} = \frac{20\,\text{m/s} + 4\,\text{m/s}}{2} = 12\,\text{m/s}$$

  Step 2   Calculate the distance travelled.

$$\text{distance travelled} = \text{average speed} \times \text{time} = 12\,\text{m/s} \times 10\,\text{s} = 120\,\text{m}$$

In 10 s, the distance travelled is 120 m.

Questions

2.12 A stone is dropped over a cliff. Its acceleration is 10 m/s². It hits the ground after 3 s.

  a How fast will it be falling after 1 s? ... after 2 s?

  b What will its average speed be during its 3 s fall?

  c How high is the cliff?

2.13 A stone is catapulted upwards with an initial speed of 100 m/s. Its deceleration is 10 m/s² (i.e. it slows down).

  a How fast will it be moving after 5 s? ... after 10 s?

  b How high will it be after 5 s? ... after 10 s?

2.14 A car is advertised as accelerating from 0 m/s to 24 m/s in 8.0 s.

  a What is its acceleration?

  b How far does it travel in 8.0 s?

2.15 An astronaut throws a stone upwards from the surface of the Moon. Its initial speed is 8 m/s and its deceleration is 1.6 m/s².

  a How long will it take the stone to reach its highest point (at which speed = 0 m/s)?

  b How high will it go?

◆ TOPIC 3 FORCE, MASS AND ACCELERATION

A **force** will make an object accelerate. The acceleration produced depends on the size of the force and the mass of the object:

force (newtons, N) = mass (kg) × acceleration (m/s^2) $F = m \times a$

$$\text{acceleration} = \frac{\text{force}}{\text{mass}} \qquad a = \frac{F}{m}$$

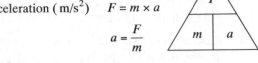

UNITS

The standard unit of force is the newton.
1 N will give a mass of 1 kg an acceleration of 1 m/s^2.

$$1 \text{ N} = 1 \text{ kg m/s}^2$$

Where masses are given in grams or tonnes in a question, change them into kilograms before calculating forces or accelerations.

1 g	= 0.001 kg
1000 g	= 1 kg
1000 kg	= 1 tonne

WORKED EXAMPLE 3A

Question

What force is needed to give a mass of 30 kg an acceleration of 0.5 m/s^2?

Answer

Step 1   Write down what you know, and what you want to know.

$m = 30$ kg
$a = 0.5$ m/s^2
$F = ?$

Step 2   Use the triangle to find the appropriate form of the equation.

$F = m \times a$

Step 3   Substitute in the values and work out the answer.

$F = 30 \text{ kg} \times 0.5 \text{ m/s}^2 = 15$ N

The force required is 15 N.

Questions

3.1 What force is needed to give an object of mass 20 kg an acceleration of 5 m/s²?

3.2 A force of 500 N acts on an object of mass 80 kg. What acceleration does the force produce?

3.3 What force is needed to give a spacecraft of mass 20 000 kg an acceleration of 25 m/s²?

3.4 A machine can provide a pulling force of 70 N. It is used to pull a trolley of mass 120 kg carrying bricks of mass 20 kg. What acceleration does it produce?

Take care with the units in questions 3.5 to 3.7.

3.5 What force is needed to give a 100 g pebble an acceleration of 5 m/s²?

3.6 What acceleration is produced when a force of 10 N is used to swat a fly of mass 0.1 g?

3.7 A lorry of mass 5 tonnes can accelerate at 1.5 m/s². What force does its engine supply to achieve this?

In these questions, you will have to use ideas from topics 1 and 2.

3.8 A small trolley, of mass 2 kg, is pulled by a force of 3 N.
 a What is its acceleration?
 b How fast will it be moving after 2 s, if it starts from rest?
 c How far will it travel in this time?

3.9 A car accelerates from rest to a speed of 20 m/s in 10 s. Its mass is 600 kg.
 a What force does the engine provide?
 b If the car had an extra load of 300 kg, how long would it take to reach 20 m/s?

◆ MASS AND WEIGHT

The force of **gravity** will make an object accelerate. The acceleration caused by gravity near the Earth's surface is about 10 m/s².

mass = m

weight = mg

Another way to express this is to say that the strength of the Earth's gravitational field (g) is 10 N/kg. An object of mass 1 kg has a **weight** of 10 N:

weight (N) = mass (kg) × g (m/s² or N/kg)

$$W = m \times g$$

Near the Earth's surface, g = 10 N/kg = 10 m/s²

Do not confuse g (acceleration caused by gravity) with g for grams!

Questions

3.10 What is the weight of each of the following?
  a an apple of mass 0.1 kg
  b a ball of mass 2 kg
  c a person of mass 60 kg
  d a car of mass 500 kg
  e a lorry of mass 3 tonnes
  f a ship of mass 6000 tonnes
  g a marble of mass 10 g
  h a fly of mass 0.05 g

3.11 What are the mass and the weight of each of the objects in question 3.10 on the surface of the Moon, where $g = 1.6$ N/kg?

3.12 Estimate the mass and the weight of this book.

◆ UNBALANCED FORCES

If two or more forces are acting on an object, you must work out their combined effect (the **resultant force**) before you can work out the acceleration they produce.

WORKED EXAMPLE 3B

Question

What is the resultant force acting on this object? What acceleration does it produce?

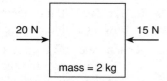

20 N   15 N

mass = 2 kg

Answer

Step 1 Decide which force is the greater. In this case, the greater force is 20 N, acting to the right.

Step 2 Calculate the resultant force by adding or subtracting the other forces, according to their directions. In this case, the only other force is 15 N acting to the left.

resultant force = 20 N − 15 N = 5 N acting to the right.

Step 3 Calculate the acceleration.

$$a = \frac{F}{m} = \frac{5\,\text{N}}{2\,\text{kg}} = 2.5\,\text{m/s}^2$$

The acceleration produced is 2.5 m/s^2.

Questions

3.13 For each of these diagrams, work out the resultant force acting on the object, and the acceleration produced.

a

```
10 N →   [ m = 5 kg ]   ← 20 N
```

b

```
5 N →   [ m = 4 kg ]   ← 15 N
```

c

```
                      40 N →
20 N →   [ m = 1 kg ]
                      ← 60 N
```

d

```
           ↓ 20 N
10 N →   [ m = 40 kg ]   ← 30 N
           ↑ 20 N
```

3.14 A car's engine provides a force of 700 N to propel it forwards. There is a frictional force of 400 N opposing the car's motion. If the mass of the car is 600 kg, what is its acceleration?

3.15 A sky rocket has a mass of 0.5 kg. The burning fuel produces a force of 15 N upwards.
  a What is the weight of the rocket?
  b Draw a diagram to show the two forces acting on the rocket as it leaves the ground.
  c What is the resultant force acting on the rocket?
  d What acceleration does this produce?

◆ TOPIC 4 ENERGY

The **kinetic energy** (KE or E_k) is the energy an object has because of its movement. It depends on the mass and the speed of the object:

kinetic energy (J) $= \frac{1}{2} \times$ mass (kg) $\times$ [speed (m/s)]^2 $E_k = \frac{1}{2}mv^2$

If we know the kinetic energy of an object, and its mass, we can work out its speed:

$$\text{speed} = \sqrt{\frac{2 \times \text{kinetic energy}}{\text{mass}}} \qquad v = \sqrt{\frac{2 \times E_k}{m}}$$

The **gravitational potential energy** (GPE or E_p) is the energy an object has when it has been lifted up against the force of gravity:

Strictly speaking, this is the *change* in gravitational potential energy. An object has GPE even when it is sitting on the surface of the Earth, before it is lifted up.

gravitational potential energy (J)
= weight (N) × vertical height (m)

Near the Earth's surface, $E_p = mgh$ where $g = 10 \ \text{m/s}^2$.

UNITS

Energy may be measured in joules (J), kJ or MJ.

1000 J = 1 kJ   1 000 000 J = 1 MJ

It is safest always to work in these standard units.

WORKED EXAMPLE 4A

Question

Calculate the kinetic energy of a 60 kg athlete running at 10 m/s.

Answer

Step 1   Write down what you know, $m = 60$ kg
and what you want to know. $v = 10$ m/s
$E_k = ?$

Note that only the value of v is squared. If you work out $\frac{1}{2} \times m \times v = 300$ and then square the answer, giving 90 000, it will be incorrect.

Step 2   Write down the equation for $E_k = \frac{1}{2}mv^2$
kinetic energy.

Step 3   Substitute in the values and work out the answer.

$$E_k = \frac{1}{2} \times 60 \,\text{kg} \times (10 \,\text{m/s})^2 = \frac{1}{2} \times 60 \times 100 = 3000 \,\text{J}$$

The kinetic energy of the runner is 3000 J.

WORKED EXAMPLE 4B

Question

Calculate the increase in gravitational potential energy when a 60 kg mountaineer climbs to the top of a mountain 2000 m high.

Answer

Step 1 Write down what you know, and what you want to know.

$m = 60$ kg
$g = 10$ m/s^2
$h = 2000$ m
$E_p = ?$

Step 2 Write down the equation for gravitational potential energy.

$E_p = mgh$

Step 3 Substitute in the values and work out the answer.

$$E_p = 60 \text{ kg} \times 10 \text{ m/s}^2 \times 2000 \text{ m} = 1\ 200\ 000 \text{ J}$$

The increase in gravitational potential energy is 1 200 000 J.

Questions

4.1 Calculate the kinetic energy of each of the following:
a a stone of mass 0.1 kg moving at 20 m/s
b a brick of mass 5 kg falling at 10 m/s
c a skydiver of mass 50 kg falling at 50 m/s
d a car of mass 600 kg moving at 30 m/s
e a bee of mass 1 g flying at 5 m/s

4.2 An object of mass 2 kg has 400 J of kinetic energy. What is its speed?

4.3 Calculate the change in gravitational potential energy in each case:
a A book of mass 1 kg is lifted up 0.6 m from the floor onto a table.
b A rocket of mass 500 kg rises 5000 m into the air.
c A stone of mass 0.2 kg falls from the top of a 60 m high cliff.
d A truckload of coal, mass 20 tonnes, is lifted to the top of a 40 m high chute. (1 tonne = 1000 kg)

4.4 A student throws a ball of mass 0.4 kg upwards at 20 m/s. It has kinetic energy when it leaves her hand; it has gravitational potential energy when it reaches its highest point.
a How much kinetic energy does it have when it leaves the student's hand?
b How much gravitational potential energy has it gained when it reaches its highest point?
c How high will it go?

4.5 The student in question 4.4 drops the ball from the top of a building 5 m high. How fast will it be moving when it hits the ground?

15

◆ TOPIC 5 MOMENTUM

The **momentum** of an object depends on its mass and its velocity:

momentum (kg m/s) = mass (kg) × velocity (m/s) $p = mv$

UNITS

Units of momentum are simply kg m/s (or N s).

Questions

5.1 Calculate the momentum of each of the following:
  a a stone of mass 0.1 kg moving at 20 m/s
  b a brick of mass 5 kg falling at 10 m/s
  c a skydiver of mass 50 kg falling at 50 m/s
  d a car of mass 600 kg moving at 30 m/s
  e a bee of mass 1 g flying at 5 m/s.

5.2 a Which has more momentum, a 110 kg rugby forward running at 5 m/s or a 65 kg winger running at 8 m/s?
  b Which has more kinetic energy (see topic 4)?

◆ COLLISIONS AND EXPLOSIONS

When objects collide, the total amount of momentum is the same after the event as it was before it. Momentum is **conserved**.

A stationary object has no momentum. If it explodes, the *total* momentum of the moving parts is still zero. Again, momentum is conserved.

The idea of **conservation of momentum** can be used to solve problems involving collisions and explosions. It usually helps to draw a before-and-after diagram.

WORKED EXAMPLE 5A

Question

A 1 kg trolley moving at 6 m/s collides with a 2 kg mass. They stick together and carry on moving. What velocity do they have after the collision?

Answer

Step 1   Draw a before-and-after diagram. Mark on it what you know and what you want to know.

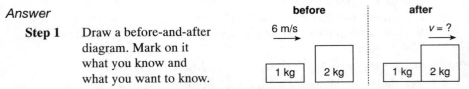

Step 2   Since momentum is conserved, we can write:

total momentum before = total momentum after

Step 3   Use the equation

momentum = mv

to work out the momentum of the trolley before the collision, and of the trolley + mass after the collision.

$$1 \text{ kg} \times 6 \text{ m/s} = 3 \text{ kg} \times v$$
$$6 \text{ kg m/s} = 3 \text{ kg} \times v$$

Step 4   Rearrange and find v.

$$v = \frac{6 \text{ kg m/s}}{3 \text{ kg}} = 2 \text{ m/s}$$

> You could probably see this intuitively: the mass of the 'trolley' increases by a factor of 3, so its final velocity is one-third of its initial value.

The final speed of the trolley is 2 m/s.

WORKED EXAMPLE 5B

Question

Suppose the 2 kg mass had been moving in the same direction as the trolley at a speed of 3 m/s. How fast would the trolley now move after the collision?

Answer

Step 1   Follow the same steps as in worked example 5A.

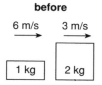

Step 2   total momentum before = total momentum after

Step 3   In this case, we have two moving objects before the collision. We have to work out the momentum of each of them separately, and then add them together.

$$1 \text{ kg} \times 6 \text{ m/s} + 2 \text{ kg} \times 3 \text{ m/s} = 3 \text{ kg} \times v$$
$$6 \text{ kg m/s} + 6 \text{ kg m/s} = 3 \text{ kg} \times v$$
$$12 \text{ kg m/s} = 3 \text{ kg} \times v$$

Step 4 $v = \dfrac{12 \text{ kg m/s}}{3 \text{ kg}} = 4 \text{ m/s}$

The final speed of the trolley is 4 m/s.

17

WORKED EXAMPLE 5C

Question

An astronaut of mass 80 kg is working in deep space, where there is no gravity. He throws a spanner of mass 1 kg to another astronaut, at a speed of 4 m/s. How fast does the first astronaut recoil?

Answer

In this example, the astronaut and spanner have no momentum before the 'explosion' (the moment when the astronaut throws the spanner). He moves in the opposite direction to the spanner.

Step 1   Since there is no momentum before the explosion, you can simply draw a diagram of the situation after the event. Mark on the diagram what you know and what you want to know.

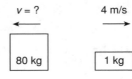

Step 2   For the case of this explosion, we can write:

momentum to left = momentum to right

Step 3   Using the equation momentum = mv, substitute in the values and work out the answer.

$$80 \text{ kg} \times v = 1 \text{ kg} \times 4 \text{ m/s}$$
$$80 \text{ kg} \times v = 4 \text{ kg m/s}$$

$$v = \frac{4 \text{ kg m/s}}{80 \text{ kg}} = 0.05 \text{ m/s}$$

The astronaut recoils at 0.05 m/s. (He is in danger of drifting off further into space!)

Questions

Before tackling each of these questions, decide whether it describes a 'collision' or an 'explosion'.

5.3 A 50 kg girl steps at 4 m/s out of a dinghy of mass 200 kg. How fast does the dinghy begin to move backwards?

5.4 A railway wagon of mass 600 kg is moving at 5 m/s. It collides with a stationary truck of mass 900 kg. At what speed do they move off together?

5.5 A 1000 kg gun fires a 30 kg shell horizontally with a velocity of 500 m/s. Find the recoil velocity of the gun.

5.6 A child is playing with a bat and ball. The bat, of mass 2 kg and moving at 10 m/s, hits the stationary ball, of mass 0.25 kg. If the ball flies off at 40 m/s, how fast does the bat move after the impact?

MACHINES

◆ TOPIC 6 WORK

When a force moves, it does **work**. Energy is transferred from one object to another. The energy transferred is known as the work done by the machine.

$$\text{work done (J)} = \text{force (N)} \times \begin{array}{c}\text{distance moved}\\ \text{in the direction}\\ \text{of the force (m)}\end{array} \qquad W = F \times d$$

> **UNITS**
>
> 1 joule = 1 newton × 1 metre = 1 newton-metre
> 1 J = 1 N m

WORKED EXAMPLE 6A

Question

A car travels 100 m along a road. The frictional force opposing its motion is 500 N. How much work does the car do against friction?

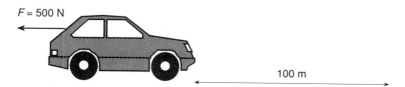

F = 500 N

100 m

Answer

Step 1   Write down the force and the distance moved. Check that the movement is in the direction of the force.

F = 500 N
d = 100 m

Both are in the same direction, along the road.

Step 2   Write down the equation, substitute in the values and calculate the answer.

$W = F \times d$
$W = 500 \text{ N} \times 100 \text{ m} = 50\,000 \text{ J}$

The work done against friction is 50 000 J.

Questions

6.1 How much work is done when a concrete block weighing 20 000 N is lifted 25 m upwards by a crane?

6.2 A mountaineer weighs 600 N. He carries a pack weighing 150 N. How much work does he do in climbing a mountain 3000 m high?

6.3 How much energy is transferred when a rock weighing 2000 N falls to the foot of a 20 m high cliff?

6.4 A chocolate bar provides 420 kJ of energy. How high could a 600 N climber climb on this supply of energy alone?

6.5 A weightlifter pushes up a 60 N weight 75 cm, and repeats this exercise a total of 20 times. Calculate the total amount of work done.

6.6 How much work is done by a child who weighs 400 N running up 30 steps, each 20 cm high?

6.7 A sports car weighing 12 000 N is driven along a 1 km stretch of road. The frictional force opposing the car is 1800 N, and the end of the road is 80 m higher than the start. How much work does the car do?

◆ TOPIC 7 POWER

Power is the rate at which energy is transferred (i.e. the rate at which work is done).

$$\text{power (watts, W)} = \frac{\text{energy transferred (J)}}{\text{time taken (s)}} \qquad P = \frac{W}{t}$$

$$\text{power} = \frac{\text{work done}}{\text{time taken}}$$

$$\text{energy transferred} = \text{power} \times \text{time taken} \qquad W = P \times t$$

See also topic 12 'Electrical power'.

UNITS

1 watt = 1 joule per second   1 W = 1 J/s

1000 W = 1 kW

1 000 000 W = 1 MW

> Take care not to confuse W for watts with W for energy transferred (or work done)!

WORKED EXAMPLE 7A

Question

A motor requires 6000 J of energy to lift a load in 15 s. What is the power of the motor?

Answer

Step 1   Write down what you know, and what you want to know.

$$W = 6000 \text{ J}$$
$$t = 15 \text{ s}$$
$$P = ?$$

Step 2   Write down the appropriate version of the equation.

$$P = \frac{W}{t}$$

Step 3   Substitute in the values and work out the answer.

$$P = \frac{6000 \text{ J}}{15 \text{ s}} = 400 \text{ W}$$

The power of the motor is 400 W.

21

PHYSICS ◆ MACHINES

Questions

7.1 How much power is developed in each of the following cases?
  a A light bulb transfers 500 J of energy in 10 s.
  b An electric heater provides 30 000 J of energy in 1 minute.
  c A horse does 1 350 000 J of work in 30 minutes.

7.2 How much energy is transferred in each of the following cases?
  a A 100 W motor works for 20 s to raise a load.
  b A 1 kW motor runs for 1 hour to drive a milkfloat.
  c A 60 W lamp is switched on for 20 minutes.
  d A 2 kW heater is switched on for 6 hours. (Give your answer in MJ.)

7.3 A gas fire consumes 180 litres of gas in an hour. Each litre of gas provides 40 kJ of energy when it is burned. What is the power supplied by the fire? (Give your answer in kW.)

7.4 The average diet of an adult in the UK supplies 10 MJ per day. What is the average power that can be dissipated by someone eating such a diet?

In questions 7.5 to 7.7, you will have to use the equation from topic 6:

  work done = force × distance moved.

7.5 How much work is done, and how much power is developed, in each of the following cases?
  a An elephant takes 100 s to pull a log 50 m. The frictional force opposing it is 4000 N.
  b A girl of weight 400 N runs up 50 steps, each 20 cm high, in 10 s.
  c A crane lifts a steel girder weighing 140 000 N to a height of 30 m in exactly one minute.

7.6 A racing cyclist pedals for 6 km against a total resistive force of 75 N in 300 s. What is the cyclist's average power?

7.7 A 2 kW motor raises a skip weighing 4000 N to a height of 10 m. How long does it take?

◆ TOPIC 8 EFFICIENCY

The **efficiency** of a process or device is the fraction of the energy supplied that is transferred usefully.

$$\text{efficiency} = \frac{\text{useful work done}}{\text{energy supplied}} \times 100\%$$

$$\text{efficiency} = \frac{\text{useful power out}}{\text{power supplied}} \times 100\%$$

UNITS

Efficiency has *no* units: it is a fraction or a percentage.

Note that both the useful work done and the energy supplied must be in the same units (both J, or both kJ, etc.). Similarly, useful power out and power supplied must both have the same units (both W, or both kW, etc.).

WORKED EXAMPLE 8A

Question

8000 J of electrical energy is supplied to a motor which drives a pulley. The pulley raises a 300 N load by 20 m. What is the efficiency of the motor?

Answer

Step 1   Work out the amount of useful work done. In this case, a load is lifted, so we use

$$\text{work done} = \text{force} \times \text{distance moved}$$
$$W = F \times d = 300 \text{ N} \times 20 \text{ m} = 6000 \text{ J}$$

Step 2   Work out the energy supplied. In this case, the amount is given in the question.

energy supplied = 8000 J

Step 3   Use the equation to calculate the efficiency.

$$\text{efficiency} = \frac{\text{useful work done}}{\text{energy supplied}} \times 100\%$$

$$= \frac{6000 \text{ J}}{8000 \text{ J}} \times 100\% = 75\%$$

The efficiency of the motor is 75%.

PHYSICS ◆ MACHINES

Questions

In the questions which follow, you may have to use ideas from topics 6 and 7.

8.1 Copy and complete the table below. Which is the most efficient of these machines?

	Car	Steam train	Bicycle
Energy supplied per second	150 kJ	80 MJ	1200 J
Work done per second	45 kJ	4 MJ	960 J
Efficiency			

8.2 Copy and complete the table below. Which is the most efficient of these machines?

	Machine A	Machine B	Machine C
Energy supplied	2000 J	2000 J	4000 J
Load	550 N	25 N	1600 N
Distance moved by load	3 m	60 m	2 m
Work done on load			
Efficiency			

8.3 An electric light bulb requires 100 W of electrical power. It provides 50 J of light energy in 1 minute. How efficient is it?

8.4 An immersion heater requires 1000 W of electrical power. How long would it take to supply 60 000 J to the water tank if it was 100% efficient? How long would it take if it was only 80% efficient?

8.5 A man pulls a rope to make a pulley system lift a load. He provides a force of 150 N, and pulls the rope 4 m. The pulley system lifts a 500 N load up through a distance of 1 m.
 a How much work does the man do?
 b How much work is done on the load?
 c What is the efficiency of the pulley system?

8.6 A power station burns 30 tonnes of coal each minute. Each tonne of coal provides 27 000 000 000 J of energy. If the electrical power output of the power station is 5000 MW, how efficient is it?

8.7 A forklift truck is 75% efficient. If it is supplied with 1 kJ of energy, how high can it raise a 500 N load?

◆ TOPIC 9 MOMENTS

The turning effect of a force is called its **moment**.

moment of a force (N m) = force (N) × perpendicular distance from pivot to line of action of the force (m) $M = F \times x$

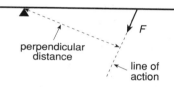

Distances *must* be measured from the pivot to the line of action of the force; usually the correct distances will be given in the question.

If you always do remember about perpendicular distances, you may find it easier to remember the equation as:

moment = force × distance from pivot

When an object is balanced:

sum of clockwise moments = sum of anticlockwise moments

UNITS

The standard unit of moment is the newton-metre, N m. Sometimes it is more convenient to work with distances in cm or mm.

◆ SOLVING PROBLEMS

It is important to do the following things:

◆ Decide where the pivot is.
◆ Decide whether the object is balanced or unbalanced.
◆ For each force, decide whether the force is tending to turn the object clockwise or anticlockwise.

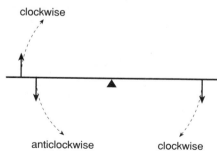

◆ Decide whether any distance given in the question is the *perpendicular* distance from the pivot to the line of action of the force.

WORKED EXAMPLE 9A

Question

The beam shown here is balanced. What is the size of force X?

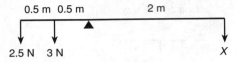

0.5 m 0.5 m   2 m

2.5 N   3 N   X

Answer

In this case, the pivot is shown clearly in the question, you are told that the beam is balanced, and all the distances shown are measured from the pivot and are perpendicular to the line of action of the force.

Step 1   Write down the equation for a balanced object.

sum of clockwise moments = sum of anticlockwise moments

Step 2   Write down the clockwise moments, and put this equal to the anticlockwise moments. In this example, only force X is clockwise.

$$X \times 2 \text{ m} = (3 \text{ N} \times 0.5 \text{ m}) + (2.5 \text{ N} \times 1 \text{ m})$$

Step 3   Multiply out and simplify the right-hand side.

$$X \times 2 \text{ m} = 1.5 \text{ N m} + 2.5 \text{ N m} = 4.0 \text{ N m}$$

Step 4   Rearrange to find the value of X.

$$X = \frac{4.0 \text{ N m}}{2 \text{ m}} = 2 \text{ N}$$

> It would be incorrect to add up the forces and multiply by the sum of the distances:
> $X \times 2 \text{ m} \neq (3 \text{ N} + 2.5 \text{ N}) \times (0.5 \text{ m} + 1 \text{ m})$
> $= 8.25 \text{ N m}$

The size of force X is 2 N.

Questions

9.1 Calculate the moment in N m of each of the forces shown here. Say whether each one is acting clockwise or anticlockwise.

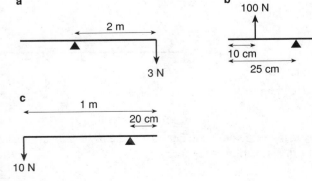

a

2 m

3 N

b

100 N

10 cm

25 cm

c

1 m

20 cm

10 N

9.2 In each of these diagrams, the object shown is balanced. Calculate the unknown force X or the unknown distance x.

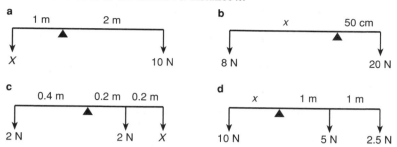

a
1 m 2 m
X 10 N

b
x 50 cm
8 N 20 N

c
0.4 m 0.2 m 0.2 m
2 N 2 N X

d
x 1 m 1 m
10 N 5 N 2.5 N

9.3 Is this object balanced? If not, in which direction will it tend to turn?

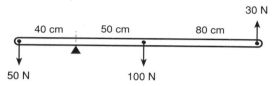

30 N
40 cm 50 cm 80 cm
50 N 100 N

9.4 Student A weighs 500 N and is holding 12 bricks, each of which weighs 20 N. Student B weighs 400 N and is holding five similar bricks. They are sitting on the ends of the seesaw. How many bricks must A pass to B for the seesaw to balance?

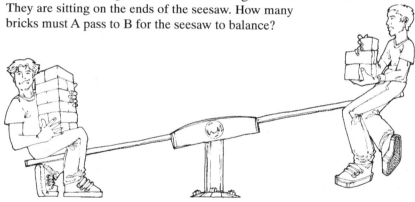

9.5 This object is acted on by several forces. Which force has no turning effect?

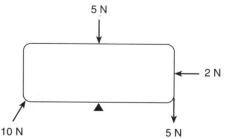

5 N
2 N
10 N 5 N

◆ TOPIC 10 WAVES

The speed (v), frequency (f) and wavelength (λ) of a wave are related by this equation:

speed (m/s) = frequency (hertz, Hz) × wavelength (m) $v = f \times \lambda$

$$\text{frequency} = \frac{\text{speed}}{\text{wavelength}} \qquad f = \frac{v}{\lambda}$$

$$\text{wavelength} = \frac{\text{speed}}{\text{frequency}} \qquad \lambda = \frac{v}{f}$$

UNITS

The frequency f is measured in hertz, Hz. 1 Hz = 1 wave per second.

1 kHz = 1000 Hz
1 MHz = 1 000 000 Hz

The wavelength λ is measured in metres, m. (λ is lambda, Greek letter l.)

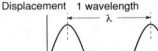

1 km = 1000 m
1 mm = 0.001 m

WORKED EXAMPLE 10A

Question

BBC Radio broadcasts signals on Long Wave with frequency 200 kHz and wavelength 1500 m. What is the speed of these signals?

Answer

| Step 1 | Write down what you know, and what you want to know. | f = 200 kHz = 200 000 Hz
λ = 1500 m
v = ? |

Step 2 Write down the form of the equation $v = f \times \lambda$
which you require. Use the triangle
if it helps.

Step 3 Substitute in the values and work out the answer.

$v = 200\ 000\ \text{Hz} \times 1500\ \text{m} = 300\ 000\ 000\ \text{m/s}$

The speed of radio waves is 300 000 000 m/s.

Questions

10.1 What is the speed of sound in steel, if ultrasonic waves of frequency
30 000 Hz travelling through a steel bar have wavelength 0.2 m?

10.2 Sound travels at different speeds through different gases. The table shows the
wavelength of sound waves, frequency 2 kHz, in four different gases.
Calculate the speed of sound in each.

Gas	Wavelength (m)
hydrogen	0.635
nitrogen	0.170
oxygen	0.160
chlorine	0.106

10.3 Some ripples in a ripple tank are produced at a frequency of 20 Hz. If they
travel across the water at a speed of 0.4 m/s, what is their wavelength? (Give
your answer in m, and in cm.)

10.4 We can see light in the visible spectrum, from red to violet. The table shows
the shortest and longest wavelengths which we can see. Calculate the
corresponding frequencies.

Colour	Wavelength (m)
red	0.000 000 750
violet	0.000 000 400

Speed of light = 300 000 000 m/s

10.5 Copy and complete the table below.

Wave	Wavelength (m)	Frequency (Hz)	Speed (m/s)
water waves	100	0.05	
sound in lead		325	1 300
radio (MW)	240		300 000 000
microwaves	0.03		300 000 000
green light in glass		600 000 000 000 000	200 000 000

29

PHYSICS ◆ WAVES

In questions 10.6 to 10.8, you will have to use information in the question to work out one of the quantities, before you can use the equation $v = f \times \lambda$.

10.6 When testing a 300 m long steel bridge, engineers used ultrasound waves of frequency 200 000 Hz. These waves were found to travel from one end of the bridge to the other in 0.05 s.
  a What was the speed of sound in the steel bridge?
  b What was the wavelength of the ultrasound in the steel?

10.7 Students measuring the speed of waves on the sea find that four waves pass the end of the pier in 20 s. They measure the wavelength of the waves, and find that it is 12 m. What is the speed of the waves?

10.8 The diagram is based on a photo of a vibrating string, 120 cm long. If the source of the vibrations has a frequency of 50 Hz, what is the speed of the waves along the string?

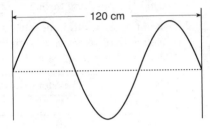

◆ MEASURING FREQUENCY WITH AN OSCILLOSCOPE

WORKED EXAMPLE 10B

Question

The oscilloscope timebase was set at 0.1 s per division to obtain the trace shown. What is the frequency of the electrical waves shown?

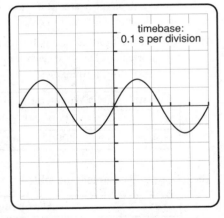

Note that we are measuring horizontally.

Answer

Step 1 Work out the number of divisions for one complete wave.

Two waves occupy ten divisions, so one wave occupies five divisions.

Step 2 Write down the timebase setting.
  timebase setting = 0.1 s/div

Step 3 Multiply the number of divisions per wave by the timebase setting to find the time for one wave.
  time for one wave = 5 div × 0.1 s/div = 0.5 s

Step 4   Work out the reciprocal of this quantity to find the frequency.

$$\text{frequency} = \frac{1}{0.5\,\text{s}} = 2\,\text{Hz}$$

Reciprocal means '1 over', or 1/x on a calculator.

The frequency of the electrical waves is 2 Hz.

Questions

10.9 This oscilloscope screen shows two traces.

  a Which trace has the higher frequency? Explain how you can tell from the trace.

  b Calculate the frequency of each trace.

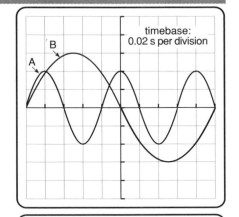

timebase: 0.02 s per division

10.10 The trace shown here was made by connecting a microphone to an oscilloscope and playing a recorder into it.

  a What is the frequency of the note shown?

  b What is the wavelength of the note shown? (The speed of sound in air is 330 m/s.)

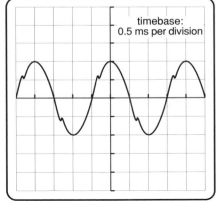

timebase: 0.5 ms per division

10.11 The trace shown was made by connecting a mains power supply to an oscilloscope.

  a What is the frequency of the mains supply?

  b Draw the trace you would expect to see if the timebase control was changed to 2 ms/div (0.002 s/div).

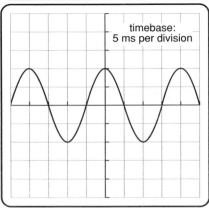

timebase: 5 ms per division

31

◆ TOPIC 11 RESISTANCE

The **electrical resistance** of a component tells us the voltage (potential difference, p.d.) needed to make a current of 1 A flow through it.

1 Ω requires 1 V to make 1 A flow through it.   1 Ω = 1 V/A

resistance (ohms, Ω) = $\dfrac{\text{potential difference (volts, V)}}{\text{current (amperes, A)}}$

$R = \dfrac{V}{I}$ $V = I \times R$ $I = \dfrac{V}{R}$

UNITS

Resistance is measured in ohms, Ω.

$$1000 \ \Omega = 1 \ k\Omega$$
$$1\,000\,000 \ \Omega = 1 \ M\Omega$$

WORKED EXAMPLE 11A

Question

What is the resistance of a lamp if a potential difference of 24 V makes a current of 3 A flow through it?

Answer

Step 1   Write down what you know, and what you want to know.

$V = 24$ V
$I = 3$ A
$R = ?$

Step 2   Use the triangle to find the required form of the equation.

$R = \dfrac{V}{I}$

Step 3   Substitute in the equation and work out the answer.

$R = \dfrac{24 \text{ V}}{3 \text{ A}} = 8 \Omega$

So the resistance of the lamp is 8 Ω.

32

Questions

11.1 What is the resistance of a light bulb which has a current of 0.25 A flowing through it when it is connected to the 240 V mains?

11.2 What potential difference is needed to make a current of 2.5 A flow through a 18 Ω resistor?

11.3 What current will flow through a 400 Ω resistor when it is connected to a 10 V power supply?

11.4 Copy and complete the table below.

Component	p.d. (V)	Current (A)	Resistance (Ω)
A	240	2.0	
B		6.0	0.5
C	240		15
D		0.005	400
E	1.5		100

11.5 For each of these circuits, calculate the readings on the meters shown:

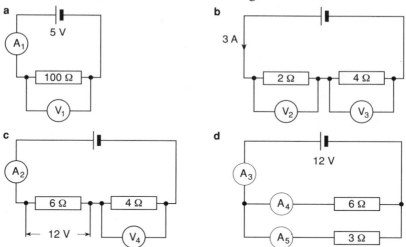

11.6 For each of these circuits, calculate the resistances of the resistors shown:

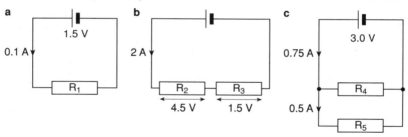

33

11.7 A light-dependent resistor is connected up to a 12 V supply. In bright daylight, it is found to let through a current of 0.4 A; in a dark room, the current flowing is 0.02 A. What are the values of its resistance in bright light, and in the dark?

11.8 **Data analysis** A student measured the resistance of a thermistor at several different temperatures. The table shows the results.

Temperature (°C)	25	40	50	65	78	89	100
Potential difference (V)	12	12	12	12	12	12	12
Current (A)	0.02	0.03	0.04	0.08	0.12	0.16	0.20

a Copy the table, and add a fourth row to show calculated values of the resistance of the thermistor.
b Plot a graph to show how the resistance changes with temperature.
c Write a sentence to summarize what the graph shows you.

◆ OHM'S LAW

An electrical component follows Ohm's Law if its resistance is the same no matter what current flows through it, that is

$$R = \frac{V}{I} = \text{constant}$$

There are two ways to check whether a component follows Ohm's Law:

◆ Calculate $R = \frac{V}{I}$; see if the value is the same for all values of current.
◆ Draw a graph of current against potential difference; if the component follows Ohm's Law, it will be a straight line passing through the origin. In the graph here, only component A follows Ohm's Law.

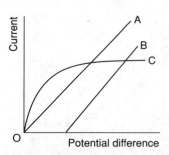

WORKED EXAMPLE 11B

Question

In measurements of the resistance of an electrical heater, a student found the following results:

Genuine experimental results would never be as perfect as this

Potential difference (V)	3.0	6.0	9.0	12.0
Current (A)	0.5	1.0	1.5	2.0

Does the resistance of the heater obey Ohm's Law?

Answer

You can see from the figures that, as the p.d. increases in equal steps, so does the current. This suggests that the heater's resistance does indeed follow Ohm's Law. Here are two ways to check:

Method 1   Copy the table and add a third row for the resistance. Calculate the resistance using $R = \dfrac{V}{I}$.

Potential difference (V)	3.0	6.0	9.0	12.0
Current (A)	0.5	1.0	1.5	2.0
Resistance (Ω)	6.0	6.0	6.0	6.0

Since $R = 6.0\ \Omega$ for all values of the p.d., it follows that the heater's resistance obeys Ohm's Law.

Method 2   Draw a graph of current against potential difference:

Since this is a straight line passing through the origin, it follows that the resistance of the heater obeys Ohm's Law.

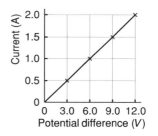

Questions

11.9 This graph shows how current depends on p.d. for four different components.
  a Which two components have resistances that follow Ohm's Law?
  b Which of these has the greater resistance?
  c Which component has a resistance which increases as the voltage increases?
  d Which component has a resistance which decreases as the voltage increases?

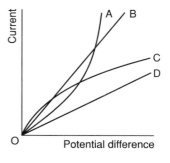

11.10 The table shows measurements for a light bulb. The potential difference across it was gradually increased, and the current through it measured.

Potential difference (V)	2.0	4.0	6.0	8.0	10.0	12.0
Current (A)		0.10	0.18	0.25	0.31	0.36	0.40

  a Draw a graph and use it to decide whether the resistance of the light bulb follows Ohm's Law.
  b What is the greatest value of the bulb's resistance?

35

◆ TOPIC 12 ELECTRICAL POWER

We use electric current to carry energy from one place to another. **Power** tells us about the rate at which energy is being transferred in a circuit. For an electric circuit, we can calculate the power using this equation:

power = potential difference × current $\quad P = V \times I$
(watts, W) (volts, V) (amps, A)

People often remember this as:

watts = volts × amps

WORKED EXAMPLE 12A

Question

A current of 0.25 A flows through a 240 V light bulb. What is the power rating of the bulb?

Answer

Step 1 Write down what you know, and $\quad V = 240$ V
what you want to know. $\quad I = 0.25$ A
$\quad P = ?$

Step 2 Use the triangle to find a suitable $\quad P = V \times I$
form of the equation.

Step 3 Substitute in the values and work out the answer.
$P = 240$ V $\times 0.25$ A $= 60$ W

The power rating of the light bulb is 60 W.

WORKED EXAMPLE 12B

Question

A microwave cooker is rated at 1000 W, and operates from the 240 V mains supply. Would a 3 A fuse be suitable to protect the cooker?

Answer

In this example, we are first going to have to find the current which normally flows through the cooker. To do this follow the same three steps as in worked example 12A.

Step 1 $\quad P = 1000$ W
$\quad V = 240$ V
$\quad I = ?$

Step 2 $\quad I = \dfrac{P}{V}$

Step 3 $\quad I = \dfrac{1000\,\text{W}}{240\,\text{V}} = 4.2\,\text{A}$

So a current of 4.2 A normally flows through the cooker.

Step 4 The fuse must not blow when 4.2 A is flowing: it has to protect the cooker from currents which are *higher* than this. So a 3 A fuse will not do. (In practice, a 13 A fuse would be fitted.)

Questions

12.1 A current of 5 A flows through a heater when it is connected to the 240 V mains. What is its power?

12.2 A car headlamp bulb is rated at 36 W. It runs off the car's 12 V battery. What current flows through the bulb when it is working?

12.3 A loudspeaker is labelled '30 W – maximum safe current 5 A'. What is the greatest potential difference which could safely be connected across it?

12.4 What is the maximum power of the appliances which can be connected safely to a standard 13 A, 240 V socket? (Give your answer in W, and in kW.)

12.5 An electric cooker has an oven rated at 3 kW, a grill rated at 2 kW, and four rings each rated at 500 W. The cooker operates from the 250 V mains. Would a 30 A fuse be suitable for the cooker?

12.6 How many 150 W lamps can safely be run from a 240 V supply fitted with a 3 A fuse?

◆ POWER, ENERGY AND MONEY

Power has an important meaning *wherever* energy is being transferred, not just in electric circuits:

$$\text{power (watts, W)} = \frac{\text{energy transferred (joules, J)}}{\text{time (seconds, s)}} \qquad P = \frac{E}{t}$$

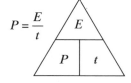

energy transferred (J) = power (W) × time (s)

$$1\,\text{W} = 1\,\text{J/s}$$

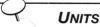

UNITS

Power: 1000 W = 1 kW
Energy: 1000 J = 1 kJ

1 kW h (1 kilowatt-hour) is the energy transferred by a 1 kW device in one hour. Energy in kW h is calculated using this form of the equation:

energy transferred (kW h) = power (kW) × time (h)

A 'unit' of electricity is 1 kW h, or 3 600 000 J. If we know the cost of one unit, we can calculate the cost of using an appliance.

WORKED EXAMPLE 12C

Question

A greenhouse heater rated at 500 W is left running overnight for ten hours. What is the cost of this, if each unit of electricity costs 8p?

Answer

Step 1   Calculate the number of units used. Remember that power must be in kW.

$$P = \frac{E}{t} = 500 \text{ W} = 0.5 \text{ kW}$$

$$t = 10 \text{ h}$$

energy = 0.5 kW × 10 h = 5 kW h = 5 units

Step 2   Calculate the cost.

cost = 5 units × 8p/unit = 40p

So the cost of using the heater is 40p.

Questions

12.7 How much energy is transferred when a 100 W lamp is switched on for 10 s? ... for one minute?

12.8 How long does it take for a 100 W lamp to transfer 1 kW h of energy?

12.9 How much does it cost to run a 3 kW heater for five hours, if one unit costs 8p?

12.10 A 6 V battery makes a current of 4 A flow through a heater for ten minutes. What is the power of the heater? How much energy is transferred in this time?

12.11 How much energy does a 12 V, 3 A car lamp transfer in 10 s?

12.12 A central heating pump is on from 5 am to 10 am each morning, and from 6 pm to 11 pm each evening. If the pump is rated at 50 W, how many units of electricity does it need each day? What is the cost of this, if one unit costs 8p?

12.13 Which is more expensive, leaving a 100 W lamp on for a day, or using a 2 kW heater for one hour?

12.14 The illustration shows the information on an electricity bill. Calculate the number of units used at each tariff, and the total cost of the electricity used.

Northern
Electricity

You can make enquiries to
PO BOX 2000
NORTHCASTLE

You can phone us on
012-843-XXX

MS A B OTHER
12 ANY STREET
NORTHCASTLE

Previous Reading	Present Reading	Tariff	Units used	Price per unit		Amount £ p
13740	13945	FULL		8.2p		
2096	3466	OFF-PEAK		2.1p		

TOTAL CHARGES (EXCLUDING VAT))

PAYMENT DUE BY 1 DECEMBER 1995

◆ *POWER AND RESISTANCE*

Sometimes we know the resistance of a device. We can still calculate its power, provided we know either the potential difference across it or the current flowing through it. We have to use the equation

potential difference (V) = current (A) × resistance (Ω)

$$V = I \times R$$

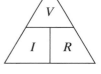

WORKED EXAMPLE 12D

Question

A 100 W heating coil is connected to a 5 V power supply. What power does it provide?

Answer

Step 1   Calculate the current which flows through the heating coil.

$$I = \frac{V}{R} = \frac{5\,V}{100\,\Omega} = 0.05\,A$$

Step 2   Calculate the power.

$$P = V \times I = 5\,V \times 0.05\,A = 0.25\,W$$

The power provided by the heating coil is 0.25 W.

Questions

12.15   What current flows when a 10 Ω resistor is connected to a 12 V car battery? What power is transferred?

12.16   A current of 5 A flows through a resistance of 2 Ω. What is the potential difference across the resistance? What power is transferred?

12.17   Copy and complete the table below.

Appliance	Power	Current	Potential difference	Resistance
immersion heater	3 kW		250 V	
lamp		0.4 A	250 V	
loudspeaker	20 W			5 Ω
torch bulb	1.5 W		2.5 V	

12.18   A transformer is connected to a 12 V supply, and a current of 2.5 A flows through its primary windings. The transformer supplies a current of 0.1 A at a potential difference of 240 V from its secondary windings. Calculate:
   a the power supplied to the primary windings
   b the power supplied by the secondary windings
   c the power wasted in the transformer itself

◆ TOPIC 13 ELECTRIC CHARGE

An electric current is a flow of **electric charge** around a circuit. A current of one ampere flows when one coulomb passes a point in a circuit each second.

$$\text{current (amperes, A)} = \frac{\text{charge (coulombs, C)}}{\text{time (seconds, s)}}$$

$$I = \frac{Q}{t} \qquad 1\,A = 1\,C/s$$

$$\text{charge} = \text{current} \times \text{time}$$
$$Q = I \times t \qquad 1\,C = 1\,A \times 1\,s$$

You will need to use the equation $Q = I \times t$ again in topic 30, on electrolysis.

WORKED EXAMPLE 13A

Question

The current through a car headlamp is 3 A. What charge flows through the lamp in 10 s?

Answer

Step 1   Write down what you know, and what you want to know.

$I = 3\,A$
$t = 10\,s$
$Q = ?$

Step 2   Use the triangle to find the correct form of the equation.

$Q = I \times t$

Step 3   Substitute in the values, and work out the answer.

$Q = 3\,A \times 10\,s = 30\,C$

The charge flowing through the lamp is 30 C.

Questions

13.1 What current flows when 36 C of charge flows past a point in a circuit in one minute?

13.2 A flashbulb requires a current of 5 A. The flash lasts 0.02 s. How much charge flows through the bulb in this time?

13.3 A rechargeable battery stores 7200 C of charge. For how long can it make a current of 4 A flow through a resistor?

13.4 What charge flows through a transistor if a current of 20 mA flows for ten minutes? (1 mA = 0.001 A)

13.5 A car battery is labelled '160 A h': it can supply a current of 160 A for one hour. For how long could it supply a current of 5 A?

You will need to make use of other electrical equations from topics 11 and 12 in questions 13.6 to 13.11.

13.6 A 12 V battery is connected across a 60 Ω resistor. How much charge flows through the resistor in 1 s? ... in one minute?

13.7 What potential difference is needed to make 40 C of charge flow through a 20 Ω resistor in 5 s?

13.8 What current flows through this resistor? How much charge flows through it in 20 s?

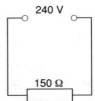

13.9 The graph shows how the current through a lamp depends on the potential difference across it. How much charge flows through the lamp in one minute when the p.d. across it is 6 V?

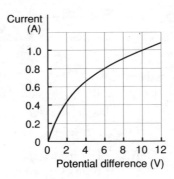

13.10 A torch bulb is labelled '3 V, 0.6 W'. How much charge flows through the bulb in one minute in normal use?

13.11 A 1 kW heater is connected to a 250 V supply.
   a How much charge flows through the heater each second?
   b How much energy is transferred to the heater each second?
   c How much energy does each coulomb of charge transfer to the heater?

MATTER

◆ TOPIC 14 DENSITY

The density of a material tells us the mass (in kg) of 1 m^3 of the material.

$$\text{density (kg/m}^3) = \frac{\text{mass (kg)}}{\text{volume (m}^3)} \qquad D = \frac{M}{V}$$

$$\text{mass} = \text{volume} \times \text{density} \qquad M = V \times D$$

$$\text{volume} = \frac{\text{mass}}{\text{density}} \qquad V = \frac{M}{D}$$

UNITS

The standard unit of density is kg/m^3. You may also come across

$$\text{density (g/cm}^3) = \frac{\text{mass (g)}}{\text{volume (cm}^3)} \qquad \text{density (g/litre)} = \frac{\text{mass (g)}}{\text{volume (litres)}}$$

Volume: $1000 \text{ cm}^3 = 1 \text{ litre}$
$1\,000\,000 \text{ cm}^3 = 1 \text{ m}^3$
$1 \text{ cm}^3 = 1 \text{ ml (millilitre)}$
$1 \text{ dm}^3 = 1 \text{ litre}$

Mass: $1000 \text{ g} = 1 \text{ kg}$
Density: $1 \text{ g/cm}^3 = 1000 \text{ kg/m}^3$
$1 \text{ g/cm}^3 = 1 \text{ kg/litre}$

WORKED EXAMPLE 14A

Question

A block of lead has a volume of 0.5 m³. Its mass is 5700 kg. What is its density?

Answer

Step 1 Write down what you know, and what you want to know.

$M = 5700 \text{ kg}$
$V = 0.5 \text{ m}^3$
$D = ?$

> Don't forget the units!

Step 2 Use the triangle to decide how to find the answer – the density.

$$D = \frac{M}{V}$$

Step 3 Use the figures given to work out the answer.

$$D = \frac{5700 \text{ kg}}{0.5 \text{ m}^3} = 11400 \text{ kg/m}^3$$

The density of lead is $11\,400 \text{ kg/m}^3$.

Questions

14.1 A block of aluminium has a mass of 108 kg, and its volume is 0.04 m³. What is the density of aluminium?

14.2 A full bucket contains 20 kg of water. What is the volume of the bucket? (Density of water = 1000 kg/m³)

14.3 A barometer is to be filled with 0.001 m³ of mercury. It is more accurate to weigh the mercury, rather than to measure its volume. What is the mass of this volume of mercury? (Density of mercury = 13 600 kg/m³)

14.4 Copy and complete the table below.

Object	Mass (kg)	Volume (m³)	Density (kg/m³)
W	5 000	2	
X	20 000		4000
Y		6	3000
Z	10 000		5000

14.5 A supplier's catalogue offers blocks of tungsten (mass 38.6 g, volume 2 cm³), and rods of wolfram (mass 96.5 g, volume 5 cm³). Which has the greater density, tungsten or wolfram?

In questions 14.6 to 14.10, you will have to work out the volume or mass from information given in the question.

14.6 What is the volume of air in a lab of dimensions 8 m × 5 m × 3 m? What is the mass of the air? (Density of air = 1.3 kg/m³)

14.7 A brick has dimensions 8 cm × 10 cm × 25 cm. Its mass is 3.6 kg. What is the density of the brick, in g/cm³?

14.8 A steel cube has sides of length 10 cm. What is its mass? (Density of steel = 7.7 g/cm³)

14.9 A stone has mass 80 g. When it is submerged in water in a measuring cylinder, the level rises from 120 cm³ to 160 cm³. What is the volume of the stone? What is its density?

14.10 A student is measuring the density of ethanol. She makes the following measurements: mass of empty bottle = 28.7 g, mass of water-filled bottle = 78.7 g, mass of alcohol-filled bottle = 68.7 g. If she knows that the density of water is 1 g/cm³, what is the density of ethanol?

14.11 How much does 1000 cm³ of water weigh? How much does the same volume of mercury weigh? (Density of water = 1 g/cm³; density of mercury = 13.6 g/cm³)

> You will need to use the fact that 1 kg of mass has a weight of about 10 N (10 newtons) on the Earth's surface.

14.12 An apple is found to weigh 1 N. Its volume is 125 cm³. Would it float on water?

TOPIC 15 PRESSURE

Pressure tells us about the force acting on 1 m² of a surface. All fluids (liquids and gases) exert a pressure. Solids also exert pressure, because of their weight.

$$\text{pressure (Pa)} = \frac{\text{force (N)}}{\text{area (m}^2\text{)}} \qquad P = \frac{F}{A}$$

force (N) = pressure (Pa) × area (m²)

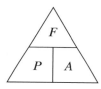

UNITS

Pressure: 1 pascal (Pa) is the same as 1 N/m².

You may also come across pressure in kN/m² (kPa) or N/cm².

Area: 1 cm² = 0.0001 m²
        1 mm² = 0.000 001 m²
        1 m² = 10 000 cm²
        1 m² = 1 000 000 mm²

Force: 1 kN = 1000 N

The table lists the value of atmospheric pressure on Earth in a number of different units.

Unit	Atmospheric pressure
Pa	100 000 Pa
N/cm²	10 N/cm²
atmosphere	1 atm
bar	1 bar
millibar	1000 mbar
psi	15 psi

1 psi = 1 pound per square inch

WORKED EXAMPLE 15A

Question

A force of 200 N is exerted on a surface of area 5 m^2. What pressure results?

Answer

Step 1	Write down what you know, and what you want to know.	$F = 200$ N $A = 5$ m^2 $P = ?$
Step 2	Use the triangle to decide how to find the required answer – the pressure.	$P = \dfrac{F}{A}$
Step 3	Use the figures given to work out the answer.	*Don't forget the units!*

$$P = \frac{200\,\text{N}}{5\,\text{m}^2} = 40\,\text{Pa} \ \ (\text{or } 40\ \text{N/m}^2)$$

The pressure is 40 Pa.

Questions

15.1 An athlete is standing with both feet flat on the ground. When running, she has only one foot on the ground at a time. Is the pressure she exerts on the ground greater or less than when she is standing still?

15.2 A cyclist and his cycle weigh 800 N. The total area of the tyres in contact with the ground is 0.001 m^2. What is the pressure on the ground?
Later, the cyclist notices that one of the tyres is flat, so that the area of contact with the ground is greater. Will the pressure now be greater or less?

15.3 In a hydraulic jack, the oil pressure is 500 000 Pa. What force will the oil exert on a piston of area 0.2 m^2?
What force on a smaller piston, of area 0.04 m^2, is needed to create this pressure?

15.4 Copy and complete the table below.

Force (N)	Area (m^2)	Pressure (Pa)
300	2	
100 000	0.1	
	10	250
	0.001	50 000

In questions 15.5 to 15.8, you will have to take care with the units.

15.5 A force of 100 kN acts on a surface of area 20 m². What pressure does this create? (Give your answer in Pa.)

15.6 The steel bar shown in the drawing weighs 28 N. What pressure does it exert when lying as shown? What pressure would it exert if it were standing on end? (Give your answers in N/cm².)

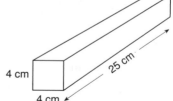

4 cm

4 cm

25 cm

15.7 A hammer strikes a nail with a force of 500 N. The head of the nail has area 0.1 cm²; its point has area 0.01 cm². Calculate the pressure the hammer exerts on the head of the nail, and the pressure which the point of the nail exerts on the wood.

15.8 Concrete can withstand a pressure of 50 000 000 Pa without crumbling. An engineer has designed a bridge weighing 1500 kN. This force must be supported on piers whose total area is 3 m². Would concrete be strong enough for this purpose?

15.9 Copy and complete the table below. (Give your answers in the units shown.)

Force	Area	Pressure
20 kN	40 m²	Pa
300 N	15 cm²	N/cm²
N	20 m²	250 kPa
kN	10 m²	100 000 Pa

In questions 15.10 to 15.12, you will need to use the fact that the atmospheric pressure on Earth is about 100 000 Pa.

15.10 A large man has a surface area of 3 m². What force does the atmosphere exert on him?

15.11 A large window has a glass pane measuring 4 m × 2 m. What force does the atmosphere exert on the outer surface of the window? Why does the window not cave in?

15.12 The atmospheric pressure on the surface of Venus is about 9 000 000 Pa. How does this compare with the atmospheric pressure on the Earth's surface? What force would a spacecraft have to withstand on the surface of Venus, if its surface area were 5 m²?

◆ TOPIC 16 ENERGY TRANSFER

When energy is transferred to an object, its temperature may rise: the more energy, the greater the rise in temperature. The rise in temperature depends on the material from which the object is made.

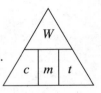

We can work out how much energy is needed as follows:

energy = specific heat capacity × mass × temperature rise
(J)   (J/kg °C)   (kg)   (°C)

$$W = c \times m \times t$$

The specific heat capacity c is a property of the material concerned.

We can use the equation in another form to find how much the temperature of an object will rise when energy is transferred to it:

$$\text{temperature rise} = \frac{\text{energy}}{\text{specific heat capacity} \times \text{mass}} \qquad t = \frac{E}{c \times m}$$

The table lists some specific heat capacities.

Material	Specific heat capacity c (J/kg °C)
water	4200
aluminium	880
lead	130
copper	380
iron	440
ice	2100
ethanol	2400
air	1000

WORKED EXAMPLE 16A

Question

A pan containing 2 kg of water at 20 °C is to be heated until it boils at 100 °C. How much energy must be transferred to the water?

> You are less likely to make mistakes if you work out the rise in temperature first, as a separate step in the calculation.

Answer

Step 1   First work out the rise in temperature.

temperature rise = final temperature – initial temperature
= 100 °C – 20 °C
= 80 °C

Step 2   Now write down what you know, and what you want to know.

c = 4200 J/kg °C
m = 2 kg
t = 80 °C
energy = ?

From the table opposite

Step 3   Use the equation to work out the energy required:

energy required = specific heat capacity × mass × temperature rise
= 4200 J/kg °C × 2 kg × 80 °C = 672 000 J
or $W = c \times m \times t$ = 4200 J/kg °C × 2 kg × 80 °C = 672 000 J

The energy required is 672 000 J. (In practice, more energy than this would be needed. The pan itself would need to be heated, and some energy would escape.)

Questions

In solving these problems, you will need to find values of the specific heat capacity of the different substances from the table opposite.

16.1 How much energy is needed to heat 1 kg of water from 0 °C to 100 °C? How much would be needed for 2 kg? ... for 0.5 kg?

16.2 How much energy is needed to heat an iceberg made of 5000 kg of ice from −20 °C to 0 °C?

16.3 A 10 kg block of iron is at a temperature of 400 °C. It has to be cooled down to 50 °C before it will be safe to handle. How much energy must be removed from it?

16.4 A bucket containing 20 kg of water is supplied with 630 000 J of energy. By how much will its temperature rise?

16.5 A 1 kg block of ice is put in a freezer. Its temperature initially is 0 °C. The freezer extracts 42 000 J of energy from it. What is its final temperature?

16.6 Which requires more energy, heating 2 kg of potatoes from 10 °C to 100 °C, or heating 6 kg of potatoes from 50 °C to 80 °C?

Usually, we cannot measure the energy supplied when heating an object directly: we may have used an electrical heater or some other means of heating. In questions 16.7 and 16.8, you will need to use the extra information given to help you to work out the energy supplied. Use the equation: energy transferred (J) = power (W) × time (s).

16.7 An electric immersion heater transfers energy at a rate of 3500 W. It is fitted in a tank containing 100 kg of water at 50 °C.
    a How much energy is required to heat the water to boiling point, 100 °C?
    b How long will it take the heater to do this?
    c How hot will the water be after one hour?

16.8 A large room contains 40 kg of air. Estimate how long it will take a 2 kW electric heater to raise the temperature of the air from 10 °C to 20 °C. Explain whether your answer is likely to be an under-estimate or an over-estimate.

◆ TOPIC 17 THE KELVIN TEMPERATURE SCALE

There are several different temperature scales. The two you will come across are:

◆ the Celsius scale (temperatures in °C)
◆ the Kelvin scale (temperatures in kelvins, K)

They are related by the equation: $K = °C + 273$ or $°C = K - 273$

WORKED EXAMPLE 17A

Question

Liquid oxygen boils at 90 K. What is this temperature in °C?

Answer

Step 1 Select the correct equation. $°C = K - 273$

Step 2 Substitute in the temperature $°C = 90 - 273 = -183 °C$
in K and calculate the answer.

Liquid oxygen boils at –183 °C.

Questions

In all of these questions, you will need to be able to convert temperatures from one scale to the other.

17.1 What are the following temperatures on the Kelvin scale?
0 °C, 27 °C, 200 °C, –27 °C, –127 °C, –100 °C

17.2 What are the following temperatures on the Celsius scale?
0 K, 100 K, 273 K, 300 K, 321 K

17.3 Which is hotter, 35 °C or 310 K?

17.4 The surface temperature of the Sun is approximately 5200 K. The
temperature at its core is approximately 14 000 000 K. What would you say
these temperatures are in °C?

17.5 Copy and complete this table:

Temperature	°C	K
absolute zero		
boiling point of nitrogen		77
freezing point of pure water		
boiling point of pure water		
normal body temperature	37	

◆ TOPIC 18 GASES UNDER PRESSURE

The volume of a fixed amount of gas is inversely proportional to its pressure if its temperature stays the same. For example, if the pressure is doubled, the volume is halved.

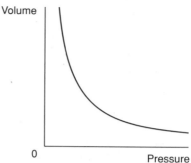

We can use the following equation to solve problems; remember that the amount of the gas and its temperature must not change.

initial pressure × initial volume = final pressure × final volume

$$P_1 \times V_1 = P_2 \times V_2$$

UNITS

Note that the units must be the same on both sides of the equation.

Pressure: pascals (Pa), atmospheres (atm), etc.

Volume: m^3, cm^3, litres, etc.

WORKED EXAMPLE 18A

Question

A syringe contains 10 cm^3 of air at a pressure of 1 atm. It is squashed so that its volume decreases to 2 cm^3. What pressure is needed to do this? (Assume that the temperature remains constant.)

Answer

Step 1 Write down what you know, and what you want to know.

$P_1 = 1 \text{ atm}$ $P_2 = ?$
$V_1 = 10 \text{ cm}^3$ $V_2 = 2 \text{ cm}^3$

Step 2 Write down the equation.

$P_1 \times V_1 = P_2 \times V_2$

Step 3 Substitute in the equation, rearrange, and work out the answer.

$$1 \,\text{atm} \times 10 \,\text{cm}^3 = P_2 \times 2 \,\text{cm}^3$$

$$P_2 = \frac{1 \,\text{atm} \times 10 \,\text{cm}^3}{2 \,\text{cm}^3} = 5 \text{ atm}$$

The pressure is 5 atmospheres. (An alternative method is given overleaf.)

51

Alternative method (working in proportions)

You need to be clear that smaller volume means greater pressure.

when volume = 10 cm^3, pressure = 1 atm

when volume = 2 cm^3, pressure = 5 atm

The volume has been divided by 5 so the pressure will have been multiplied by 5.

Questions

18.1 A bubble of air has a volume of 50 cm^3 on the sea-bed, where its pressure is 20 atm. What will its volume be when it reaches the surface, where pressure = 1 atm? Assume that its temperature remains constant as it floats upwards.

18.2 A toy balloon is filled with air at 1.1 atm pressure. What pressure would be needed to squash it to half its original volume?

18.3 50 litres of hydrogen gas at 10^5 Pa pressure are compressed into a cylinder of volume 4 litres. What pressure does the gas now have?

18.4 **Data analysis** A teacher demonstrates how the volume of some air changes as its pressure is changed. The results are shown in the table.

Pressure (kPa)	200	180	160	140	120	100
Volume (cm^3)	12	13	14	17	20	24

a Plot a graph of these results. Which result or results do you think should be checked?

b Write a sentence to say what this graph tells you.

c Copy the table, and add a third row, with values of $P \times V$.

Do your results support the idea that the quantity $P \times V$ is constant?

d What can you say about the temperature of the air in this experiment?

◆ TOPIC 19 PROTONS, NEUTRONS AND ELECTRONS

Atoms are made up of **protons**, **neutrons** and **electrons**; these are **sub-atomic** particles. Protons and neutrons make up the tiny **nucleus** of the atom. The electrons surround the nucleus.

An atom contains equal numbers of protons and electrons. As a result, it is electrically neutral.

Particle	Mass	Charge
proton	1 unit	+1
neutron	1 unit	0
electron	0	−1

We represent an atom by showing its chemical symbol, together with its proton number and its mass number:

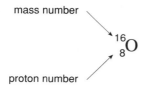

mass number

$^{16}_{8}O$

proton number

mass number   = number of protons and neutrons in the nucleus
proton number   = number of protons in nucleus
number of neutrons = mass number − proton number

◆ ISOTOPES

All atoms of a particular element have the same number of protons in their nuclei. Atoms of different **isotopes** of an element have different numbers of neutrons.

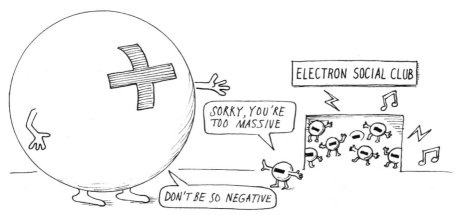

WORKED EXAMPLE 19A

Question

Find the numbers of protons, neutrons and electrons in atoms of these two isotopes of carbon:

carbon-12 $^{12}_{6}C$ carbon-13 $^{13}_{6}C$

Answer

Step 1   The symbols tell us the number of protons, and the number of protons + neutrons. Subtraction gives the number of neutrons.

Step 2   The number of electrons is the same as the number of protons in an atom.

Atom	Number of protons	Number of neutrons	Number of electrons
carbon-12	6	6	6
carbon-13	6	7	6

Questions

19.1 Write symbols for each of these atoms, showing the mass number and the proton number:

a   an atom of argon, Ar, containing 18 protons, 22 neutrons and 18 electrons

b   an atom of lithium, Li, containing 3 protons, 4 neutrons and 3 electrons.

19.2 Copy and complete the table below.

Atom		Number of protons	Number of neutrons	Number of electrons
hydrogen-1	$^{1}_{1}H$			
helium-4	$^{4}_{2}He$			
nitrogen-15	$^{15}_{7}N$			
oxygen-16	$^{16}_{8}O$			
oxygen-17	$^{17}_{8}O$			
uranium-235	$^{235}_{92}U$			
uranium-238	$^{238}_{92}U$			

19.3 a   Which pairs of atoms in the table in question 19.2 are pairs of isotopes?

b   Which two atoms have the same number of neutrons, but are isotopes of different elements?

◆ IONS

If an atom gains or loses electrons, it becomes a charged particle – an **ion**.

IONIC CHARGE

+	one fewer electron than the atom
2+	two fewer electrons than the atom
−	one more electron than the atom
2−	two more electrons than the atom

WORKED EXAMPLE 19B

Question

How many electrons are there in an O^{2-} ion? (The proton number of oxygen is 8.)

Answer

Step 1 Decide how many electrons there are in an atom of oxygen.

Oxygen's proton number is 8, so an oxygen atom has 8 electrons.

Step 2 Add or subtract according to the charge of the ion. Remember that electrons have negative charge.

The O^{2-} ion has 2 extra electrons. So, total number of electrons = 8 + 2 = 10.

Questions

19.4 How many electrons are there in a sodium ion, Na^+?
(Sodium: proton number = 11.)

19.5 Which ion has more electrons, Fe^{2+} or Fe^{3+}?

19.6 Copy and complete the table below.

Ion	Number of protons	Number of neutrons	Number of electrons
$_1^1H^+$			
$_{17}^{35}Cl^-$			
$_{17}^{37}Cl^-$			
$_{20}^{40}Ca^{2+}$			

◆ TOPIC 20 RADIOACTIVE DECAY

Radioactive substances decay more
and more slowly as time passes.
The graph shows how the number of
undecayed atoms decreases.

The half-life tells us how long it takes
for the number of undecayed atoms to
fall to half its original value:

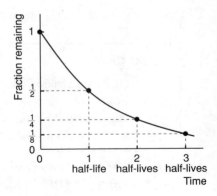

after 1 half-life, $\frac{1}{2}$ remain undecayed

after 2 half-lives, $\frac{1}{2} \times \frac{1}{2} = \frac{1}{4}$ remain undecayed

after 3 half-lives, $\frac{1}{2} \times \frac{1}{2} \times \frac{1}{2} = \frac{1}{8}$ remain undecayed

The rate of decay (as measured with a Geiger–Müller counter) also decreases
in this way.

UNITS

Half-lives are measured in seconds, minutes, hours or any other unit
of time. If you are given a graph or table of results, the half-life will
have the same units as the time.

WORKED EXAMPLE 20A

Question

*A sample of an element contains 800 undecayed atoms. The half-life of this isotope
is three days. How many atoms will remain undecayed after three days? ... after
nine days?*

Answer

Step 1 Write down the time and the half-life.

time = 3 days, 9 days
half-life = 3 days

Step 2 The number of undecayed atoms is halved after each half-life:

at first,   800 are undecayed
after 3 days,   400 remain undecayed
after 6 days,   200 remain undecayed
after 9 days,   100 remain undecayed

Number remaining after 3 days = 400. Number remaining after 9 days = 100.

WORKED EXAMPLE 20B

Question

A ratemeter was used to measure the rate of decay of a radioisotope. The graph shows how the rate changed over a period of ten hours. What is the half-life of the isotope?

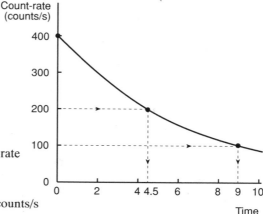

Answer

Step 1   Find the initial count-rate (when time = 0) from the graph.

     initial rate = 400 counts/s

Step 2   Divide this rate by 2, and draw across from this value on the graph.

     rate after 1 half-life = 400/2 = 200 counts/s

Step 3   Draw downwards from this point on the graph to find the half-life.

From the graph, half-life = 4.5 hours.

Check: Repeat, starting at rate = 200 counts/s.

     Step 1: initial rate = 200 counts/s
     Step 2: rate after 1 half-life = 200/2 = 100 counts/s
     Step 3: from the graph, half-life = 9.0 hours – 4.5 hours
                                   = 4.5 hours

Note that *any* two points between which the rate has halved should give the same time difference. You could try this starting at the point where rate = 300 counts/s: find how long it takes for the rate to fall to 150 counts/s.

Questions

20.1   The radioisotope carbon-11 has a half-life of 20 minutes. A sample initially contains 20 000 undecayed atoms.

   a   How many will remain undecayed after 20 minutes? ... after 80 minutes?

   b   How many will decay during the first hour?

20.2   A sample of radioactive material gives a count-rate of 3000 counts/minute. Its half-life is known to be four days.

   a   What will the count-rate be after four days? ... after twelve days?

   b   How long will it take for the count-rate to fall to 750 counts/minute?

20.3 The graph shows experimental results for a radioisotope which decays quite rapidly.

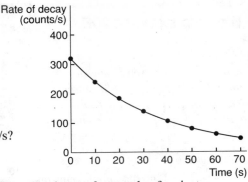

a What was the initial rate of decay?

b What was the rate of decay after 20 s?

c How long did it take for the rate of decay to fall to 70 counts/s?

d What is the half-life of this isotope?

20.4 The table gives results for the radioactive decay of a sample of an isotope. Draw a graph and use it to find the half-life of the isotope.

Time (minutes)	0	2	4	6	8	10
Rate (counts/s)	340	230	160	110	77	53

In the next question, you are given a table of data similar to that in question 20.4. You can make a good estimate of the half-life of the substance simply by carefully examining the data.

20.5 The table gives the results for the decay of a sample of protactinium-234.

Time (s)	0	30	60	90	120	150	180
Counts in 10 s	240	185	143	110	85	65	48

a What was the initial count-rate, in counts/s?

b Roughly how long did it take for the rate to fall to half of this value?

c Roughly how long did it take for the rate to fall to one quarter of its initial value?

d What is your estimate of the half-life of protactinium-234?

Background radiation is around us all the time: the reading on a Geiger–Müller counter never falls to zero. It is often important to take account of this when analysing experimental results.

20.6 The graph shows the results of an experiment in which a radioisotope from a nuclear reactor was studied.

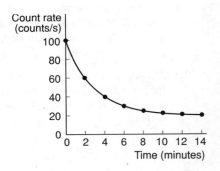

a What was the background radiation level?

b What was the half-life of the radioisotope?

c If you had not taken account of the background level, what answer would you have given for the half-life?

20.7 A student made measurements to find the half-life of a radioactive substance. She collected two sets of data.

This table shows numbers of counts in 10 s, *without the sample*:

Measurement number	1	2	3	4	5	6	7	8
Counts in 10 s	21	13	16	14	8	11	20	17

This table shows numbers of counts in 10 s, recorded every minute, *with the sample present*:

Time (minutes)	0	1	2	3	4	5	6
Counts in 10 s	85	68	53	46	38	32	26

a Use the data in the first table to calculate the average background reading.
b Copy the second table, and add a third row to show the number of counts in each 10 s interval, corrected for background radiation (by subtracting the average background reading).
c Plot a graph, and use it to deduce the half-life of the substance.

If we know the half-life of an isotope, we can use it to deduce how long a sample has been decaying for.

20.8 The half-life of carbon-14 is 5700 years. This is often used to find the age of ancient organic materials. In an investigation of charcoal from an old fire, an archaeologist found these results:
mass of ancient charcoal = 3 mg   count-rate = 60 counts/s
mass of modern charcoal = 1 mg   count-rate = 80 counts/s
a Calculate the count-rate you would expect from 1 mg of ancient charcoal.
b How many half-lives have passed since the charcoal was burned?
c How old is the charcoal?

20.9 In 1991, an ancient human body was found in the Alps, preserved in freezing conditions for thousands of years. The age of the body was established using radiocarbon dating; the graph shows a calibration curve for this technique. A sample from the body of the Iceman showed that 46% of carbon-14 had decayed since his death. When did he live?

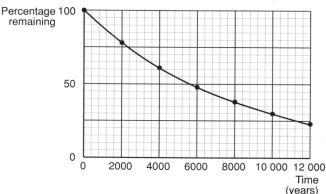

CHEMISTRY

USING SYMBOLS

◆ **TOPIC 21 CHEMICAL FORMULAS**

We use formulas to represent elements and compounds, for example, H_2 for hydrogen and CH_4 for methane. In a formula, the small number refers to the symbol written before it. If there is no small number, then it is taken to be 1; for example, in the formula H_2O, the ratio of hydrogen to oxygen is 2 : 1.

For some compounds, the formula includes brackets; for example, the formula for calcium hydroxide is $Ca(OH)_2$. The small 2 here refers to everything inside the brackets.

WORKED EXAMPLE 21A

> The formula $Ca(NO_3)_2$ is shorthand for $Ca-NO_3-NO_3$.

Question
Write down the names of the elements joined together in calcium nitrate, $Ca(NO_3)_2$, and their ratio.

Answer

    Elements: calcium nitrogen oxygen

    Ratio of the elements: calcium : nitrogen : oxygen = 1 : 2 : 6

Questions

21.1 Write down how many atoms there are in a molecule of each of the following elements:
    a hydrogen, H_2 **b** iodine, I_2
    c phosphorus, P_4 **d** sulphur, S_8

NH₃, NH₃!

21.2 For each of the following compounds, write down the names of the elements joined together and their ratio:

a carbon dioxide, CO_2
b sodium sulphide, Na_2S
c potassium hydroxide, KOH
d sulphuric acid, H_2SO_4
e glucose, $C_6H_{12}O_6$
f magnesium hydroxide, $Mg(OH)_2$
g aluminium sulphate, $Al_2(SO_4)_3$
h ammonium sulphate, $(NH_4)_2SO_4$

◆ IONIC SUBSTANCES

If we know the ions a substance is made of, we can work out its formula. Every ionic compound contains positive ions combined with negative ions. The total positive charge must equal the total negative charge so that, overall, the compound is uncharged. Ionic compounds have giant structures so we write down the simplest formula for the compound.

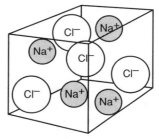

Sodium chloride contains equal numbers of positive sodium ions, Na^+, and negative chloride ions, Cl^-

WORKED EXAMPLE 21B

Question

What is the formula of magnesium nitrate?

Answer

From the table of data on page 151 you can see that the formula of a magnesium ion is Mg^{2+} and the formula of a nitrate ion is NO_3^-. A magnesium ion with a 2+ charge needs two nitrate ions, each with a 1– charge, to make the compound electrically neutral.

Ions present:	Mg^{2+}	NO_3^-
		NO_3^-
Total charge:	2+	2–

So, for every magnesium ion there are two nitrate ions.
The formula of magnesium nitrate is $Mg(NO_3)_2$.
(Remember that the small 2 outside the brackets refers to everything inside the brackets.)

CHEMISTRY ◆ USING SYMBOLS

Questions

21.3 Look at these formulas. For each one, decide whether it represents an atom, a molecule or an ion.

a He   **b** CO   **c** SO_2 **d** Li^+ **e** Ni   **f** CO_3^{2-} **g** Cl_2

21.4 Here are the formulas for the ions of some elements:

     sodium Na^+
     magnesium Mg^{2+}
     sulphur S^{2-}
     iodine I^-

Use these to write down the formulas for the following compounds:

a sodium iodide
b sodium sulphide
c magnesium sulphide
d magnesium iodide

21.5 Write down the formulas of the following compounds; you will need to use the table on page 151 to find the formulas of the relevant ions.

a potassium chloride
b sodium oxide
c magnesium bromide
d aluminium chloride
e sodium hydroxide
f zinc carbonate
g calcium nitrate
h sodium sulphate
i calcium hydrogencarbonate
j ammonium sulphate
k aluminium oxide

TOPIC 22 BALANCING CHEMICAL EQUATIONS

Follow the steps below to write a balanced symbol equation for a chemical reaction.

WORKED EXAMPLE 22A

Question
What is the balanced equation for the reaction of methane with oxygen?

Answer

Step 1   Write down the equation in words. (To do this you have to know the names of the reactants and products.)

reactants   → products
methane + oxygen → carbon dioxide + water

Step 2   Write down the formulas for the reactants and products. (Use the same steps as in worked example 21B.)

$$CH_4 + O_2 \rightarrow CO_2 + H_2O$$

Step 3   Count the atoms on both sides of the equation. If they are the same, the equation is balanced; move to step 5. If they are not, go on to step 4.

left-hand side	right-hand side
1 C atom	1 C atom
4 H atoms	2 H atoms
2 O atoms	3 O atoms

The equation is not balanced.

Use pencil here as it's often a process of trial and error!

Step 4   Balance the equation by writing numbers in front of the formulas. These numbers will refer to the **whole** formula.

$$CH_4 + 2O_2 \rightarrow CO_2 + 2H_2O$$

left-hand side	right-hand side
1 C atom	1 C atom
4 H atoms	4 H atoms
4 O atoms	4 O atoms

The equation is balanced now: there are the same numbers of atoms on both sides.

Step 5   Add state symbols (these normally show the state at room temperature):

(s) = solid
(l) = liquid
(g) = gas
(aq) = dissolved in water

$$CH_4(g) + 2O_2(g) \rightarrow CO_2(g) + 2H_2O(l)$$

Questions

22.1 Which of these equations are balanced?

    a $C(s) + O_2(g) \rightarrow CO_2(g)$

    b $NaOH(aq) + H_2SO_4(aq) \rightarrow Na_2SO_4(aq) + H_2O(l)$

    c $Fe_2O_3(s) + 2CO(g) \rightarrow 2Fe(l) + 3CO_2(g)$

    d $Li(s) + H_2O(l) \rightarrow LiOH(aq) + H_2(g)$

22.2 Write the formulas (including the state symbols) for each of the following substances:

    a nitrogen gas   **b** methane gas

    c molten aluminium   **d** solid carbon dioxide (dry ice)

    e steam   **f** salty water

    g limewater (calcium hydroxide solution)

22.3 Copy and balance the symbol equations below.

    a $Mg(s) + O_2(g) \rightarrow MgO(s)$

    b $H_2(g) + O_2(g) \rightarrow H_2O(l)$

    c $Fe(s) + HCl(aq) \rightarrow FeCl_2(aq) + H_2(g)$

    d $CuO(s) + HNO_3(aq) \rightarrow Cu(NO_3)_2(aq) + H_2O(l)$

    e $Ca(OH)_2(aq) + HCl(aq) \rightarrow CaCl_2(aq) + H_2O(l)$

    f $KHCO_3(s) + H_2SO_4(aq) \rightarrow K_2SO_4(aq) + CO_2(g) + H_2O(l)$

    g $Al(s) + Cl_2(g) \rightarrow AlCl_3(s)$

> Remember that you must **not** change any of the formulas to balance the equation.

22.4 Fill in the blanks to complete these equations.

    a This happens in the thermit reaction:

        aluminium + iron oxide $\rightarrow$ aluminium oxide + iron

          ...   + $Fe_2O_3(s)$ $\rightarrow$ $Al_2O_3(s)$ + $2Fe(s)$

    b This reaction is used in the production of titanium metal:

        titanium chloride + magnesium $\rightarrow$ magnesium chloride + titanium

          $TiCl_4(l)$ + $2Mg(s)$ $\rightarrow$ ...   + $Ti(s)$

    c Energy from glucose is transferred to you using this reaction:

        glucose + oxygen $\rightarrow$ carbon dioxide + oxygen

        $C_6H_{12}O_6 +$ ... $\rightarrow$ $6CO_2$ +   ...

22.5 Write balanced symbol equations for the reactions below. You will probably have studied them before and carried out some of them in the laboratory. Include the state symbols where you can.

    a copper reacting with oxygen to give copper oxide (CuO)

    b calcium oxide reacting with water to give calcium hydroxide solution

    c hydrogen peroxide (H_2O_2) decomposing slowly to give oxygen and water

    d nitrogen reacting with hydrogen to give ammonia (NH_3)

    e iron reacting with chlorine to give solid iron chloride ($FeCl_3$)

    f calcium carbonate reacting with dilute hydrochloric acid to give calcium chloride, carbon dioxide and water

HOW MUCH MATTER?

◆ TOPIC 23 MASSES OF ATOMS AND ELEMENTS

Of all atoms, those of hydrogen are the lightest. The **relative atomic mass** of hydrogen is 1.

All the other elements have heavier atoms than hydrogen does. Oxygen has a relative atomic mass of 16. Notice that relative atomic mass has no units because it is a ratio: the mass of each atom is being compared with that of one hydrogen atom. An oxygen atom is 16 times as heavy as a hydrogen atom.

A_r is the symbol for relative atomic mass:
$A_r(H) = 1$, $A_r(O) = 16$, $A_r(S) = 32$.

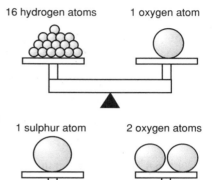

16 hydrogen atoms   1 oxygen atom

1 sulphur atom   2 oxygen atoms

Questions

You will need to use the table of data on page 150 to answer these questions.

23.1 The following elements are listed in alphabetical order: aluminium, argon, chlorine, magnesium, phosphorus, silicon, sulphur. Arrange them in order of relative atomic mass, putting the lightest first.

23.2 How many times heavier than hydrogen atoms are atoms of
  a carbon **b** magnesium **c** bromine **d** barium **e** lead?

23.3 How many times heavier is
  a a magnesium atom than a carbon atom?
  b a nitrogen atom than a lithium atom?
  c a sulphur atom than a helium atom?
  d a bromine atom than an argon atom?
  e an iron atom than a nitrogen atom?

◆ MASSES OF MOLECULES AND COMPOUNDS

Most non-metal elements consist of molecules, for example oxygen (O_2), sulphur (S_8) and hydrogen (H_2).

Most compounds of non-metals with other non-metals are also molecules; examples include water (H_2O), carbon dioxide (CO_2) and tetrachloromethane (CCl_4).

The **relative molecular mass** (M_r) tells us how heavy each molecule is compared with a hydrogen atom. The relative molecular mass of a non-metal element or a compound of non-metals can be found from the formula. All you do is add up the relative atomic masses of the elements in the molecular formula.

WORKED EXAMPLE 23A

Question
What is the relative molecular mass of ethanol, C_2H_6O?

Answer

Step 1 Write down the formula of the compound.

$$C_2H_6O$$

> Once you understand how to find M_r from the formula, you might like to take a shortcut and do steps 2 and 3 in your head.

Step 2 Write down the atoms in the formula.

$$2 \times C \qquad 6 \times H \qquad 1 \times O$$

Step 3 Write down the A_r for the elements.

$$A_r(C) = 12 \quad A_r(H) = 1 \quad A_r(O) = 16$$

Step 4 Work out the M_r for ethanol.

$$(2 \times 12) \ + \ (6 \times 1) \ + \ (1 \times 16)$$
$$= 24 + 6 + 16 = 46$$

This tells us that a molecule of ethanol is 46 times heavier than an atom of hydrogen: its relative molecular mass is 46.

Salts are **ionic** compounds: they are usually compounds of metals with one or more non-metals. They are made from **giant structures** of ions.

The **relative formula mass** (M_r) of a salt is found by adding up the relative atomic masses of the elements in the formula. Follow the same steps as in worked example 23A.

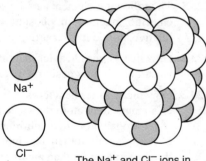

Na⁺

Cl⁻

The Na⁺ and Cl⁻ ions in sodium chloride are arranged in a **giant structure**

Questions

23.4 What are the relative molecular masses of:

    a oxygen, O_2 **b** water, H_2O

    c hydrogen iodide, HI   **d** silicon tetrachloride, $SiCl_4$?

23.5 What are the relative formula masses of:

    a potassium chloride, KCl

    b sodium oxide, Na_2O

    c aluminium bromide, $AlBr_3$

    d calcium hydrogencarbonate, $Ca(HCO_3)_2$

    e iron sulphate, $Fe_2(SO_4)_3$?

> Remember that the small numbers outside the brackets refer to everything inside them.

TOPIC 24 MOLES OF ATOMS

When comparing chemicals it is important to know you are talking about the same amount of each substance. **For chemists this means the same number of particles.** The standard amount of any substance contains the **same number of particles** as there are atoms in 1 g of hydrogen.

For carbon $A_r = 12$, so each carbon atom is 12 times heavier than a hydrogen atom. So 12 g of carbon contains the **same number** of atoms as 1 g of hydrogen.

The unit of chemical amount of substance is the **mole**. The symbol for this unit is **mol.**

If you know how many moles you need, you can work out what mass this is by using equation 1. If you know the mass of a substance, you can work out how many moles it is by using equation 2.

NOTE

Equation 1   mass of substance (g) = number of moles × mass of 1 mol (g)

Equation 2   number of moles of substance = $\dfrac{\text{mass of substance (g)}}{\text{mass of 1 mol (g)}}$

WORKED EXAMPLE 24A

Question

What is the mass of 5 mol of lithium atoms?

Answer

Step 1   Find A_r from a table.

$A_r (\text{Li}) = 7$

Step 2   Write down the mass of 1 mol of lithium atoms.

mass of 1 mol of Li = 7 g

Step 3   Scale up or down depending on the question. (Use equation 1.)

mass of 5 mol of Li $= 5 \times 7$ g
$= 35$ g

So 5 mol of lithium atoms have a mass of 35 g.

Questions

You will need to use the table of data on page 150 to find the relative atomic masses of the elements in the following questions.

24.1 What are the masses of:
  a 1 mol of sodium atoms
  b 10 mol of chlorine atoms
  c 0.1 mol of iodine atoms
  d 0.5 mol of iron atoms
  e 0.125 mol of bromine atoms?

Use equation 1 to help you answer this question.

24.2 How many moles of atoms are there in:
  a 27 g of aluminium
  b 20 g of calcium
  c 4 g of bromine
  d 140 g of nitrogen?

Use equation 2 to help you answer this question.

Use equations 1 and 2 to help you answer questions 24.3 to 24.9.

24.3 What mass of carbon contains the same number of atoms as 39 g of potassium?

24.4 What mass of sulphur contains the same number of atoms as 6 g of magnesium?

24.5 What mass of copper contains the same number of atoms as 2.07 g of lead?

24.6 What mass of fluorine contains the same number of atoms as 4000 g of helium?

24.7 How many moles of lithium contain the same number of atoms as 320 g of oxygen?

24.8 How many moles of phosphorus contain the same number of atoms as 2.0 g of neon?

24.9 How many moles of tin contain the same number of atoms as 0.201 g of mercury?

◆ MOLES OF COMPOUNDS

The mass of one mole of molecules of a substance is equal to its relative molecular mass in grams. For example, M_r for ethanol is 46: the mass of one mole of ethanol molecules is 46 g. The mass of one mole of a salt is its relative formula mass expressed in grams. For magnesium nitrate, $M_r = 148$, so the mass of one mole of magnesium nitrate is 148 g.

If we know the formula of a substance, we can work out the mass of any number of moles of the substance. We can also work out how many moles there are in a given mass of the substance.

Equations 1 and 2 on page 67 apply to **all** substances, whether they are elements or compounds.

WORKED EXAMPLE 24B

Question

What is the mass of 2 mol of sulphuric acid, H_2SO_4?

Answer

Step 1   Use Steps 1 to 4 from worked example 23A.

Formula of the compound: H_2SO_4
Atoms in the formula $2 \times H$ $1 \times S$ $4 \times O$
A_r for the elements: $A_r(H) = 1$ $A_r(S) = 32$ $A_r(O) = 16$
M_r for sulphuric acid (2×1) + (1×32) + (4×16)
                                    $= 2 + 32 + 64 = 98$

Step 2   The mass of 1 mol is its M_r, expressed in grams.

mass of 1 mol of sulphuric acid = 98 g

Step 3   Scale the quantities up or down according to the question. (Use equation 1.)

mass of 2 mol of sulphuric acid = 2 × 98 g = 196 g

So 2 mol of sulphuric acid have a mass of 196 g.

Questions

Use equation 1 to help you answer questions 24.10 and 24.11.

24.10 What are the masses of:
  a 1 mol of chlorine molecules, Cl_2
  b 2 mol of water molecules, H_2O
  c 0.5 mol of sulphur molecules, S_8
  d 0.25 mol of phosphorus molecules, P_4?

24.11 What are the masses of:
  a 1 mol of zinc sulphide, ZnS
  b 0.5 mol of lead nitrate, $Pb(NO_3)_2$
  c 5 mol of sodium sulphate, Na_2SO_4
  d 0.1 mol of ammonium chloride, NH_4Cl?

24.12 How many moles of molecules are there in:
  Use equation 2 to help you answer this question.
  a 6.4 g of sulphur dioxide, SO_2
  b 56 g of carbon monoxide, CO
  c 14 g of nitrogen, N_2
  d 160 g of bromine, Br_2
  e 4.0 g of hydrogen fluoride, HF?
  You will need to use both equations 1 and 2 to answer this question.

24.13 What mass of:
  a oxygen contains the same number of molecules as 8.0 g of sulphur, S_8?
  b water contains the same number of molecules as 22 g of carbon dioxide?

◆ MOLES OF IONS

In calcium chloride, $CaCl_2$, there are two chloride ions, Cl^-, for every calcium ion, Ca^{2+}:

$$CaCl_2 = Ca^{2+} + 2Cl^-$$
1 mol   1 mol   2 mol

So in 1 mol of calcium chloride there are 2 mol of chloride ions and 1 mol of calcium ions.

WORKED EXAMPLE 24C

Question

How many moles of sodium ions, Na^+, and carbonate ions, CO_3^{2-}, are there in 3 mol of sodium carbonate, Na_2CO_3?

Answer

In 1 mol of Na_2CO_3 there are 2 mol of Na^+ and 1 mol of CO_3^{2-}.
In 3 mol of Na_2CO_3 there are 6 mol of Na^+ and 3 mol of CO_3^{2-}.

Questions

24.14 How many moles of:
  a sodium ions are there in 1 mol of sodium chloride, NaCl?
  b bromide ions are there in 0.5 mol of barium bromide, $BaBr_2$?
  c nitrate ions are there in 2 mol of magnesium nitrate, $Mg(NO_3)_2$?
  d nitrogen atoms are there in 1 mol of ammonium sulphate, $(NH_4)_2SO_4$?

You will need to use equations 1 and 2 to answer these more difficult questions.

24.15 What are the masses of:
  a 1 mol of iron chloride, $FeCl_2$
  b 2 mol of magnesium bromide, $MgBr_2$
  c 0.5 mol of nitric acid, HNO_3
  d 0.002 mol of ethane molecules, C_2H_6
  e 10 mol of potassium atoms
  f 0.25 mol of sulphur molecules, S_8
  g 0.125 mol of sulphate ions, SO_4^{2-}?

24.16 How many moles of:
  a atoms are there in 192 g of titanium?
  b atoms are there in 14 g of iron?
  c molecules are there in 11 g of carbon dioxide, CO_2?
  d molecules are there in 7 g of ethene, C_2H_4?
  e sodium ions are there in 40 g of sodium hydroxide, NaOH?
  f carbonate ions are there in 50 g of calcium carbonate, $CaCO_3$?

◆ TOPIC 25 FINDING AND USING FORMULAS

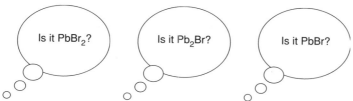

When we do an experiment to find the formula of a compound we measure the masses of the elements that combine to make it and then we convert these masses into moles. We know that equal numbers of moles contain equal numbers of particles; this means that the ratio of the moles gives us the number ratio of the atoms combining.

WORKED EXAMPLE 25A

Question

In an analysis of sodium oxide, a chemist found that 0.69 g of sodium combined with 0.24 g of oxygen. What is the formula of sodium oxide? [A_r(Na) = 23, A_r(O) = 16]

Answer

		sodium	oxygen
Step 1	Write down the masses of the elements combining.	0.69 g	0.24 g
Step 2	Use A_r to write down the mass of 1 mol of each element.	23 g	16 g
Step 3	Work out the numbers of moles combining.	$\dfrac{0.69\,g}{23\,g}$ = 0.030 mol	$\dfrac{0.24\,g}{16\,g}$ = 0.015 mol
Step 4	Divide all the numbers by the smallest one. This gives you the simplest ratio of the numbers of moles combining.	$\dfrac{0.030}{0.015} = 2$	$\dfrac{0.015}{0.015} = 1$
Step 5	Find the formula.	Na : O = 2 : 1	

The formula is Na_2O.

The results of analysing a compound are often given in the form of its **percentage composition**. For example, methane is 75% carbon and 25% hydrogen. This means that in 100 g of methane there are 75 g of carbon and 25 g of hydrogen. So the formula can be worked out as in the example above.

Questions

25.1 Work out the formula of:

a magnesium nitride, in which 3.6 g of magnesium combines with 1.4 g of nitrogen.

b methane, given that in 0.8 g of the gas there is 0.6 g of carbon, and the rest is hydrogen.

c silicon oxide, given that 6.0 g of the oxide contains 2.8 g of silicon.

d iron bromide, if 0.378 g of iron reacts with bromine to form 2.00 g of the compound.

25.2 A certain compound, which is often used as a catalyst and found as a mineral, is a black powder. Its composition is Mn = 63.2%; O = 36.8%. Find its formula. $[A_r(Mn) = 55, A_r(O) = 16]$

You will need to use the table of data on page 150 to answer questions 25.3 to 25.5.

25.3 A bright red powder known to contain only lead and oxygen is found to contain 90.55% lead. Calculate the formula of the compound.

25.4 Calculate the formulas of red and black copper oxides, using the results below.

	Mass of copper (g)	Mass of oxygen (g)
black copper oxide	8.0	2.0
red copper oxide	3.74	0.47

25.5 Students were asked to find the formulas for two samples of white mercury chloride. They weighed some mercury chloride before and after heating. Their results are shown in the table. Calculate the formulas for the two samples and comment on your answer.

	Sample 1	Sample 2
mass of mercury chloride (g)	4.47	4.40
mass of mercury formed (g)	3.80	3.24

◆ USING FORMULAS

Once the formula of a compound is known, it can be used to work out the compound's percentage composition by mass. This information can be used to show how much metal can be extracted from an ore, for instance; it can also be used to guide people in choosing which of a range of fertilizers contains the most nitrogen.

WORKED EXAMPLE 25B

Question

Ammonium nitrate, NH_4NO_3, is commonly used in fertilizers to supply nitrogen to plants. What is the percentage of nitrogen in ammonium nitrate?

Answer

Step 1   Work out M_r for the compound as in worked example 23A.

Formula of the compound: NH_4NO_3
Atoms in the formula: $2 \times N$ $4 \times H$ $3 \times O$
A_r for the elements $A_r(N) = 14$ $A_r(H) = 1$ $A_r(O) = 16$
M_r for ammonium nitrate: (2×14) + (4×1) + (3×16)
= 28 + 4 + 48
= 80

Step 2   Now we know the mass of one mole of the compound, work out the mass of the element in one mole of the compound.

mass of nitrogen in one mole of ammonium nitrate
= (2×14)
= 28

Step 3   Work out the percentage of the element in the compound.

percentage of nitrogen by mass

$= \dfrac{28}{80} \times 100$

$= 35\%$

So the percentage of nitrogen in ammonium nitrate is 35%.

Questions

25.6 Calculate the percentage of nitrogen in the following compounds, which are used as fertilizers:
a   ammonia, NH_3
b   urea, $CO(NH_2)_2$

25.7 Calculate the percentage of copper in each of these minerals:
a   cuprite, Cu_2O
b   malachite, $Cu_2(OH)_2CO_3$
c   bornite, Cu_5FeS_4

25.8 The label for a brand of 'fluoride toothpaste' states that the toothpaste contains 1% of sodium monofluorophosphate, Na_2PO_3F. What percentage of the toothpaste is fluorine?

◆ TOPIC 26 CALCULATIONS FROM EQUATIONS

An equation is a useful shorthand for reminding us what happens during a reaction: you can see what amounts react together or are formed, and you can work out what masses will react together or will be formed. This is the kind of information that allows scientists in laboratories or in vast chemical plants to work out the amounts of chemicals needed to mix the reactants in the correct proportions. The expected **yield** of products can also be calculated.

WORKED EXAMPLE 26A

Question

How much aluminium powder do you need in the thermit process to react with 8.0 g of iron oxide? [$A_r(Al) = 27$, $A_r(Fe) = 56$, $A_r(O) = 16$]

Answer

Step 1 Write the balanced equation for the reaction.

$$2Al(s) + Fe_2O_3(s) \rightarrow Al_2O_3(s) + 2Fe(s)$$

Step 2 Pick out the substances referred to in the question and write their amounts in moles under the equation – and ignore the others.

2 mol   1 mol
i.e 2 mol of Al combine with 1 mol of Fe_2O_3

Step 3 Convert the amounts in moles to masses as in worked examples 24A and 24B.

2 mol Al = 2 × 27 g = 54 g
1 mol Fe_2O_3 = (2 × 56 g) + (3 × 16 g) = 160 g

Step 4 Scale the masses to the quantities in the question. This is $\frac{8}{160} = \frac{1}{20}$ of the amount in the equation, so scale down the mass of aluminium needed.

The question refers to 8 g of iron oxide.

Mass of aluminium needed = $\frac{1}{20} \times 54\,g = 2.7\,g$

On an industrial scale, the unit of mass is the **tonne**. So long as all the masses are measured in the same units, the method of calculation is the same. In the thermit reaction given above, for example, 8 g of iron oxide react with 2.7 g of aluminium, so 8 tonnes of iron oxide react with 2.7 tonnes of aluminium.

Questions

Use worked example 26A to help you answer questions 26.1–26.4. The equations for step 1 have been given.

26.1 What mass of water is needed to convert 28 g of calcium oxide to calcium hydroxide? $[A_r(Ca) = 40, A_r(H) = 1, A_r(O) = 16]$
$$CaO(s) + H_2O(l) \rightarrow Ca(OH)_2(s)$$

26.2 What mass of sodium hydroxide would you need to neutralize 490 g of sulphuric acid? $[A_r(H) = 1, A_r(S) = 32, A_r(O) = 16, A_r(Na) = 23]$
$$H_2SO_4(aq) + 2NaOH(aq) \rightarrow Na_2SO_4(aq) + 2H_2O(l)$$

26.3 What mass of bromine is needed to react with 0.26 g of ethene?
$$C_2H_4(g) + Br_2(l) \rightarrow C_2H_4Br_2(l)$$

> You will need to use the table of data on page 150 to answer questions 26.3 to 26.5.

26.4 What mass of coke will be used up in a blast furnace in the production of 2.8 tonnes of carbon monoxide?
$$2C(s) + O_2(g) \rightarrow 2CO(g)$$

26.5 In blast furnaces, iron oxide is reduced to iron by carbon monoxide:
$$Fe_2O_3(s) + 3CO(g) \rightarrow 2Fe(s) + 3CO_2(g)$$
What mass of carbon monoxide is needed to reduce 16 tonnes of iron oxide?

26.6 What mass of copper oxide is made when 128 g of copper is completely oxidized? $[A_r(Cu) = 64, A_r(O) = 16]$
$$2Cu(s) + O_2(g) \rightarrow 2CuO(s)$$

26.7 How much lime (calcium oxide) can you get by heating 1 kg of pure limestone? $[A_r(Ca) = 40, A_r(C) = 12, A_r(O) = 16]$
$$CaCO_3(s) \rightarrow CaO(s) + CO_2(g)$$

26.8 Titanium chloride can be reduced by magnesium to titanium metal:
$$TiCl_4(l) + 2Mg(s) \rightarrow 2MgCl_2(s) + Ti(s)$$
What mass of titanium chloride would be needed to produce 480 kg of titanium metal?

> You will need to use the table of data on page 150 to answer questions 26.8 to 26.11.

26.9 What mass of ethanol is formed when 9.0 g of glucose are fermented?
$$C_6H_{12}O_6(aq) \rightarrow 2C_2H_6O(aq) + 2CO_2(g)$$

26.10 What mass of magnesium sulphate could be obtained from 1 g of magnesium oxide?
$$MgO(s) + H_2SO_4(aq) \rightarrow MgSO_4(aq) + H_2O(l)$$

26.11 Each year 200 million tonnes of new carbon monoxide are released into the atmosphere. It is thought that this is eventually converted to carbon dioxide:
$$2CO(g) + O_2(g) \rightarrow 2CO_2(g)$$
Calculate the mass of carbon dioxide produced every year by this transformation.

HOW MUCH GAS?

◆ TOPIC 27 MOLES OF GASES

Many chemical reactions involve gases. It is easier to measure the volume of a gas than its mass.

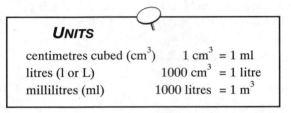

UNITS

centimetres cubed (cm^3) $1\ cm^3 = 1\ ml$

litres (l or L) $1000\ cm^3 = 1$ litre

millilitres (ml) 1000 litres $= 1\ m^3$

The volume of a given mass of gas depends on its temperature and its pressure. In order that results for different gases can be compared, the conditions under which the measurements are made must be stated.

◆ Room temperature (20 °C) and pressure (1 atmosphere) are taken to be **normal** conditions.

One mole of any gas, measured under normal conditions of temperature and pressure, occupies 24 litres. It does not make any difference what the gas is.

To solve calculations involving gas volumes, you need to use the following ideas:

1 The mass of 1 mole of gas is the relative formula mass (M_r) expressed in grams.
2 The volume of 1 mole of any gas is 24 litres (24 000 cm^3), measured at normal temperature and pressure (20 °C and one atmosphere).
3 The volume of a gas (cm^3) = number of moles of gas × volume of one mole (cm^3).

4 The number of moles of a gas = $\dfrac{\text{volume of gas } (cm^3)}{\text{volume of one mole of the gas}}$

CHEMISTRY ◆ HOW MUCH GAS?

WORKED EXAMPLE 27A

Question

What is the volume of 3 mol of helium at normal temperature and pressure?

Answer

Helium is a gas, so at room temperature and pressure

volume of 1 mol = 24 litres

volume of 3 mol = 3 × 24 litres = 72 litres.

Using ideas 2 and 3

The volume of 3 mol of helium at normal temperature and pressure is 72 litres.

Questions

27.1 Work out the volumes of the following amounts of gas, at room temperature and pressure:
a 2 mol of nitrogen
b 10 mol of hydrogen chloride
c 0.01 mol of neon
d 0.002 mol of carbon dioxide
e 0.125 mol of helium

27.2 How many moles of gas, at room temperature and pressure, are there in:
a 24 000 cm^3 of carbon dioxide
b 48 cm^3 of hydrogen
c 240 000 cm^3 of chlorine
d 3 litres of ammonia
e 72 litres of oxygen?

27.3 Work out the volumes of the following quantities of gas at room temperature and pressure:
a 2 g of hydrogen, H_2
b 3.2 g of oxygen gas, O_2
c 0.28 g of nitrogen gas, N_2
d 0.016 g of methane, CH_4

◆ TOPIC 28 CALCULATING GAS VOLUMES

Calculations from equations for reactions that involve gases are carried out in a similar way to mass calculations (Topic 26). Gas volume calculations are easier because the volume of gas (under given conditions) depends only on the amount of the gas in moles: it doesn't matter which gas is involved. Remember that this does *not* apply to solids and liquids.

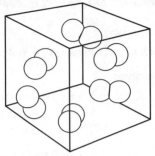

It's the **number** of molecules that decides the volume of a gas – the type of molecules doesn't matter

WORKED EXAMPLE 28A

Question

What volume of hydrogen gas can you collect when 0.35 g of lithium reacts with water at room temperature and pressure? [A_r(Li) = 7; the volume of one mole of any gas at room temperature and pressure is 24 litres.]

Answer

Step 1 Write the balanced equation: $2Li(s) + 2H_2O(l) \rightarrow 2LiOH(aq) + H_2(g)$

Step 2 Use the equation to write down the reacting amounts, in moles, of the substances in the question.   2 mol   1 mol

Step 3 Change the amounts in moles to masses – or to volumes if they are gases.

mass of 1 mol of Li = 7 g
mass of 2 mol of Li = 14 g
volume of 1 mol of hydrogen gas
= 24 litres
So 14 g of Li produces
24 litres of hydrogen gas.

Step 4 Scale the masses or volumes to the amounts mentioned in the question.

The question refers to 0.35 g of lithium.

This is $\dfrac{0.35\ g}{14\ g}$ = 0.025 of the amount

in the equation, so the volume of hydrogen formed is
0.025 × 24 litres = 0.6 litres

The volume of gas collected is 0.6 litres.

Questions

28.1 What volume of carbon dioxide, measured at room temperature and pressure, will be produced by heating 1000 g of limestone?
$[A_r(Ca) = 40, A_r(C) = 12, A_r(O) = 16]$
$$CaCO_3(s) \rightarrow CaO(s) + CO_2(g)$$

28.2 What volume of oxygen, measured under normal conditions, will be needed to completely convert 12 g of magnesium to magnesium oxide?
$[A_r(Mg) = 24, A_r(O) = 16]$
$$2Mg(s) + O_2(g) \rightarrow 2MgO(g)$$

You will need to use the table of data on page 150 to answer questions 28.3 to 28.5.

28.3 What volume of hydrogen is given off, at room temperature and pressure, when 6.5 g of zinc reacts with excess sulphuric acid?
$$Zn(s) + H_2SO_4(aq) \rightarrow ZnSO_4(aq) + H_2(g)$$

28.4 What volume of oxygen, measured under normal conditions, is given off when 1.2 g of potassium nitrate is heated?
$$2KNO_3(s) \rightarrow 2KNO_2(s) + O_2(g)$$

28.5 Carbon dioxide is often made by the reaction of hydrochloric acid on marble chips (calcium carbonate):
$$CaCO_3(s) + 2HCl(aq) \rightarrow CaCl_2(aq) + CO_2(g) + H_2O(l)$$
What mass of marble chips would you need to use to produce 3 litres of carbon dioxide at room temperature and pressure?

◆ ALL-GAS REACTIONS

Gas volume calculations are especially easy when the reactants and products involved are all gases.

◆ Equal volumes of gases contain equal numbers of moles, that is, equal numbers of particles.

This means that if you look at the ratio of moles in the equation for a reaction, it will be the same as the ratio of the gas volumes in the reaction. The worked example overleaf shows how you can use this idea to solve problems involving reactions between gases.

WORKED EXAMPLE 28B

Question

What volume of oxygen is needed to react with 40 cm^3 of methane, and what volume of carbon dioxide will be formed, if all the gas volumes are measured under the same conditions?

$$CH_4(g) + 2O_2(g) \rightarrow CO_2(g) + 2H_2O(l)$$

Answer

Step 1	Write down the equation and the reacting amounts in moles.	$CH_4(g) + 2O_2(g) \rightarrow CO_2(g) + 2H_2O(l)$ 1 mol 2 mol 1 mol
Step 2	The ratio of the volumes is the same as the ratio of the moles. Scale to the amount in the question.	1 vol 2 vol 1 vol 40 cm^3 80 cm^3 40 cm^3

So 40 cm^3 of methane reacts with 80 cm^3 of oxygen to give 40 cm^3 of carbon dioxide.

Questions

28.6 a What volume of oxygen contains the same number of molecules as 24 cm^3 of nitrogen?
b What volume of argon contains the same number of atoms as 2 cm^3 of helium?

28.7 Nitrogen oxide, NO, reacts with oxygen, O_2, to give nitrogen dioxide, NO_2. Starting with 50 cm^3 of nitrogen oxide, what volume of oxygen will be needed and what volume of nitrogen dioxide will be made, if all volumes are measured under the same conditions?
$$2NO(g) + O_2(g) \rightarrow 2NO_2(g)$$

28.8 What volume of oxygen is needed to react with 50 cm^3 of ethane, C_2H_6, when it burns and what volume of carbon dioxide will be formed?
$$2C_2H_6(g) + 7O_2(g) \rightarrow 4CO_2(g) + 6H_2O(l)$$

28.9 When 100 cm^3 of hydrogen chloride gas reacts with 80 cm^3 of ammonia, a white solid forms. There is an excess of one of the gases (some is left after the reaction has finished). Which gas is in excess, and what volume of this gas remains unreacted?
$$NH_3(g) + HCl(g) \rightarrow NH_4Cl(s)$$

28.10 Car engines burn a fuel containing octane, C_8H_{18}. What volume of oxygen, measured at room temperature and pressure, is needed to completely burn one litre of octane?
$$2C_8H_{18}(g) + 25O_2(g) \rightarrow 16CO_2(g) + 18H_2O(l)$$

HOW MUCH ELECTROLYSIS?

◆ TOPIC 29 ELECTRODE REACTIONS

◆ AT THE NEGATIVE ELECTRODE

Positive ions **gain** electrons at the negative electrode.

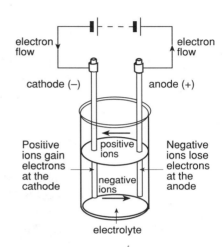

WORKED EXAMPLE 29A

Question

What is the reaction at the negative electrode when molten lead bromide, $PbBr_2$, is electrolysed using carbon electrodes? How many moles of electrons are gained by lead ions to give one mole of lead?

Answer

Step 1 Write down the equation and the ions. $PbBr_2 \rightarrow Pb^{2+} + 2Br^-$

Step 2 Write the equation for the electrode process (the half-equation). (The lead ion has a charge of **2+** and so needs **2** electrons to form a neutral atom – to be discharged). $Pb^{2+} + 2e^- \rightarrow Pb$

Step 3 In words, state what the equation tells you about the substances mentioned in the question.

$$Pb^{2+} \;+\; 2e^- \;\rightarrow\; Pb$$
$$1\ mol \quad 2\ mol \;\rightarrow\; 1\ mol$$

One mole of lead ions gains two moles of electrons to give one mole of lead.

Questions

29.1 a Complete the half-equations to show the formation of atoms from the following ions:

(i) $Na^+ + \ldots \rightarrow Na$ (ii) $\ldots + 2e^- \rightarrow Cu$
(iii) $Ni^{2+} + \ldots \rightarrow \ldots$ (iv) $Fe^{3+} + \ldots \rightarrow Fe$

b How many moles of electrons are gained by 1 mole of each of the following ions to give 1 mole of atoms?
(i) Na^+ (ii) Cu^{2+} (iii) Ni^{2+} (iv) Fe^{3+}

> Use the completed half-equations from part **a** to answer part **b**.

29.2 How many moles of electrons are needed to give
  a 0.2 mol of sodium from sodium ions, Na^+?
  b 0.25 mol of copper from copper ions, Cu^{2+}?
  c 0.5 mol of nickel from nickel ions, Ni^{2+}?

29.3 a How many moles of atoms are formed from the following ions by the gain
  of 0.6 mol of electrons?
  (i) Na^+ (ii) Cu^{2+} (iii) Ni^{2+} (iv) Fe^{3+}
  b What mass of the following elements is formed from the ions by the gain
  of 0.6 mol of electrons at the cathode? [A_r: Na = 23, Cu = 64, Ni = 59, Fe = 56]
  (i) sodium   (ii) copper   (iii) nickel   (iv) iron

29.4 How many moles of electrons are needed:
  a to change 2 mol of hydrogen ions into hydrogen molecules?
  b to form 0.1 mol of hydrogen molecules from hydrogen ions?
  c to form 2 mol of hydrogen molecules from hydrogen ions?

29.5 What volume of hydrogen gas can be
obtained, at room temperature and pressuzre,
  a from 2 mol of hydrogen ions?
  b when hydrogen ions gain 1 mol of electrons?

> Recall that the volume of 1 mol of any gas, measured at room temperature and pressure, is 24 litres.

◆ AT THE POSITIVE ELECTRODE

Negative ions **lose** electrons at the positive electrode.

WORKED EXAMPLE 29B

Question

Write down the half-equation for the reaction at the positive electrode when copper chloride is electrolysed using carbon electrodes. How many moles of ions are released to the positive electrode by the chloride ions to give one mole of chlorine molecules?

Answer

Step 1	Write down the half-equation	$Cl^- - e^- \rightarrow Cl$
Step 2	Write the equation for the formation of one molecule, Cl_2	$Cl + Cl \rightarrow Cl_2$
Step 3	Balance the equations from steps 1 and 2 and write in the reacting amounts in moles	$2Cl^- - 2e^- \rightarrow 2Cl$ 2 mol 2 mol 2 mol $2Cl \rightarrow Cl_2$ 2 mol 1 mol
	Overall,	$2Cl^- - 2e^- \rightarrow Cl_2$

When 1 mole of chorine molecules are formed, 2 moles of electrons are released.

Questions

29.6 Complete the half-equations to show the formation of atoms or molecules from the following ions:

a $Cl^- - ... \rightarrow Cl$ **b** $Br^- ... \rightarrow Br$

c $... - e^- \rightarrow I$ **d** $... - 2e^- \rightarrow Cl_2$

e $2I^- - 2e^- \rightarrow ...$

29.7 How many moles of electrons are released when:

a 1 mol of chloride ions become chlorine molecules, Cl_2?

b 0.2 mol of bromide ions (Br^-) become bromine molecules, Br_2?

c 0.1 mol of chlorine molecules are formed from chloride ions?

29.8 How many moles of chlorine molecules are released by the loss of:

a 0.2 mol of electrons from chloride ions?

b 0.5 mol of electrons from chloride ions?

> Recall that the volume of 1 mol of any gas, measured at room temperature and pressure, is 24 litres.

29.9 What volume of chlorine is released at the positive electrode, at room temperature and pressure, when:

a 0.4 mol of chloride ions become chlorine molecules?

b chloride ions release 0.2 mol of electrons?

29.10 What mass of iodine $[A_r(I) = 127]$ is obtained at the positive electrode when:

a 0.2 mol of iodine ions, I^-, become iodine molecules, I_2?

b iodide ions release 0.1 mol of electrons?

During the electrolysis of solutions of compounds that do not contain halide ions, oxygen (from the water) is formed at the positive electrode:

$$4OH^- \;-\; 4e^- \;\rightarrow\; O_2 \;+\; 2H_2O$$
$$\text{4 mol} \qquad \text{4 mol} \qquad \text{1 mol} \qquad \text{2 mol}$$

29.11 How many moles of:

a oxygen molecules are released from 1 mol of hydroxide ions?

b oxygen molecules are released when hydroxide ions lose 0.8 mol of electrons?

c electrons are lost to the positive electrode when 0.3 mol of oxygen is made?

When the electrodes are made from metals, for example copper or zinc, the metal electrode actually takes part in the reaction at the positive electrode.

29.12 When copper sulphate $(CuSO_4)$ is electrolysed using copper electrodes, copper atoms in the positive electrode become copper ions (Cu^{2+}) in the solution. $[A_r(Cu) = 64]$

$$Cu(s) - 2e^- \rightarrow Cu^{2+}(aq)$$

a How many moles of copper atoms form ions as 0.1 mol of electrons are lost at the positive electrode?

b What mass of copper dissolves from the positive electrode?

◆ TOPIC 30 *THE CHARGE NEEDED TO PRODUCE ONE MOLE*

amount of electric charge = current × time
  (coulombs, C)   (amperes, A)   (s)

$$Q = I \times t$$

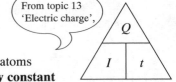

From topic 13
'Electric charge',

The minimum charge needed to deposit one mole of atoms
of an element is 96 500 C. This is called the **Faraday constant**
and is the same as the charge carried by one mole of electrons.

amount of electric charge = amount of electrons × Faraday constant
        (C)   (mol)   (C/mol)

amount of electric charge (C) = amount of electrons (mol) × 96 500 (C/mol)

$$\text{amount of electrons (mol)} = \frac{\text{amount of charge (C)}}{96\,500\,\text{C/mol}}$$

WORKED EXAMPLE 30A

Question

*How many moles of electrons flow past a point in a circuit when a current of 0.4 A
is used for 1930 s?*

Answer

Step 1   Work out the amount   charge = 0.4 A × 1930 s
       of electric charge.   = 772 C

Step 2   Use the Faraday constant to find the number of moles of electrons.

$$\text{number of moles of electrons} = \frac{772\,\text{C}}{96\,500\,\text{C/mol}} = 0.008\,\text{mol}$$

0.008 moles of electrons flow past a point in the circuit.

Questions

30.1 How many moles of electrons carry the following amounts of electric charge?
  a 48 250 C   **b** 9650 C   **c** 1930 C   **d** 482.5 C

30.2 How many moles of electrons flow past a point in a circuit when:
  a a current of 0.1 A flows for 1930 s?
  b a current of 0.8 A flows for 20 minutes and 6 seconds? (Remember to
  convert time to seconds.)

30.3 How much electric charge is carried by:
  a 2 mol of electrons?   **b** 0.3 mol of electrons?

◆ TOPIC 31 ELECTROLYSIS CALCULATIONS

◆ CALCULATING THE MASS OR VOLUME PRODUCED

If you know the charge on the ions involved in electrolysis, and the amount of charge used, you can calculate the amount in moles, or the mass, of the product formed.

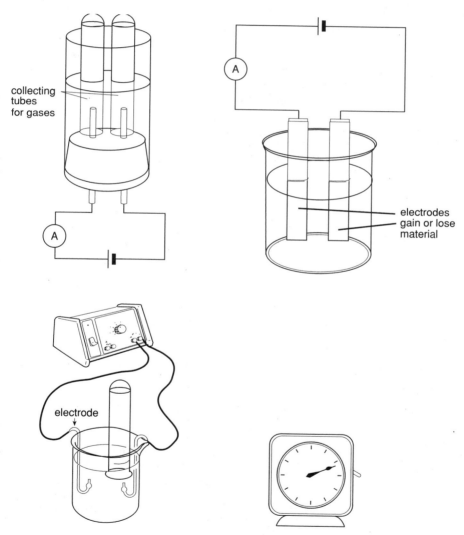

collecting
tubes
for gases

electrodes
gain or lose
material

electrode

Apparatus to discover how much of a product is formed by electrolysis

WORKED EXAMPLE 31A

Question

In the electrolysis of lead bromide ($PbBr_2$), what mass of lead is formed at the negative electrode when a current of 1 A flows for 965 s? [$A_r(Pb) = 207$]

Answer

Step 1   Work out the amount of electric charge used.

$$charge = 1 \text{ A} \times 965 \text{ s}$$
$$= 965 \text{ C}$$

Step 2   Use the Faraday constant to work out the number of moles of electrons involved.

$$moles \text{ of electrons} = \frac{965\,C}{96\,500\,C/mol}$$
$$= 0.01 \text{ mol}$$

Step 3   Write the half-equation for the reaction at the negative electrode.

$$Pb^{2+} + 2e^- \rightarrow Pb$$

Step 4   Work out the number of moles of product (here lead) formed.

$$2 \text{ mol } e^- \rightarrow 1 \text{ mol Pb}$$
$$0.01 \text{ mol } e^- \rightarrow \tfrac{1}{2} \times 0.01 \text{ mol Pb}$$
$$= 0.005 \text{ mol Pb}$$

Step 5   Convert the amount in moles to mass (or to volume if a gas is produced).

mass of 1 mol of lead = 207 g
mass of 0.005 mol of lead
$$= 0.005 \times 207 \text{ g} = 1.035 \text{ g}$$

1.035 g of lead are formed at the negative electrode.

Questions

In questions 31.1 and 31.2, step 1 has been done for you and the ion symbols are shown in brackets.

31.1 How many moles of atoms of the following elements are formed when 9650 C of electric charge is used in an electrolysis cell?
    a sodium (Na^+) **b** copper (Cu^{2+}) **c** aluminium (Al^{3+})

Use the table of data on page 150 to find A_r for the elements in these questions.

31.2 What mass of each of the following elements is formed when 1930 C of electric charge is used?
    a silver (Ag^+)   **b** lead (Pb^{2+})   **c** iron (Fe^{3+})

31.3 What mass of nickel is formed at the negative electrode when a solution of nickel chloride, $NiCl_2$, is electrolysed using a current of 0.5 A for 772 s?

31.4 When copper sulphate solution is electrolysed using copper electrodes, copper [A_r(Cu) = 64] is deposited at the negative electrode. At the same time, the positive electrode dissolves, giving copper ions, Cu^{2+}. If a current of 0.2 A flows through the cell for 2895 s,

a what mass of copper is formed at the negative electrode?
b what mass of copper is lost from the positive electrode?

31.5 Chlorine gas, Cl_2, is released at the positive electrode when sodium chloride solution is electrolysed. Find the volume of chlorine formed, at room temperature and pressure, when a current of 1 A flows for 965 s. (Remember that the volume of one mole of any gas, measured at room temperature and pressure, is 24 litres.)

◆ **WORKING OUT HOW MUCH CURRENT OR TIME WILL BE NEEDED**

Follow the steps of worked example 31A in reverse to answer these questions.

Questions

31.6 How much electric charge is needed to liberate
a 0.1 mol of silver from silver ions (Ag^+)?
b 0.2 mol of copper from copper ions (Cu^{2+})?
c 1 mol of aluminium from aluminium ions (Al^{3+})?
d 0.1 mol of hydrogen (H_2) from hydrogen ions (H^+)?

31.7 For how long will an electric current of 1 A need to flow to liberate 0.1 mol of each of the following elements at the negative electrode?
a nickel from nickel ions (Ni^{2+})
b aluminium from aluminium ions (Al^{3+})

31.8 A bead of lead of mass 0.414 g is formed at the negative electrode during the electrolysis of lead bromide ($PbBr_2$) using a current of 0.5 A. For how long did the current flow? [A_r(Pb) = 207]

31.9 Hydrogen is liberated at the negative electrode when dilute sulphuric acid is electrolysed. Calculate the current needed to give 96 cm^3 of hydrogen in 16 minutes at room temperature and pressure. (1 mol of gas at room temperature occupies 24 litres.)

Remember that, if the positive electrode is made from metal low in the reactivity series, the electrode takes part in the reaction.

31.10 How long will it take to dissolve away a copper electrode of mass 3.2 g during the electrolysis of copper sulphate ($CuSO_4$) with copper electrodes, using a current of 0.5 A? [A_r(Cu) = 64]

31.11 What current is needed to plate a cathode with 0.108 g of silver in 100 minutes? The electrolyte is a solution containing silver ions, Ag^+. (Check the units used for time.)

◆ TOPIC 32 CHARGES ON IONS

In any electrolysis calculation, if you are told the amount of electric charge used and the amount of product made, you can work out the charge on the ions involved.

WORKED EXAMPLE 32A

$[A_r(Mg) = 24]$

Question

When molten magnesium chloride is electrolysed using a current of 0.8 A for 965 s, 0.096 g of magnesium is formed. What is the charge on the magnesium ion?

Answer

Step 1 Work out the amount of electric charge.

charge = 0.8 A × 965 s
= 772 C

Step 2 Use the Faraday constant (see topic 30) to work out the number of moles of electrons involved.

moles of electrons
$$= \frac{772\,C}{96\,500\,C/mol} = 0.008\ mol$$

Step 3 Work out the number of moles of product (here magnesium) formed.

moles of magnesium $= \dfrac{0.096\,g}{24\,g}$
= 0.004 mol

Step 4 Work out the number of moles of electrons needed to produce 1 mol of product (here magnesium) at the electrode.

0.004 mol of magnesium is formed from 0.008 mol e$^-$
1 mol of magnesium is formed from $\dfrac{0.008\,mol}{0.004\,mol} \times 1 = 2$ mol e$^-$

Step 5 Write the electrode equation.

$Mg^{2+} + 2e^- \rightarrow Mg$

The charge on the magnesium ion is 2+.

Questions

> Step 1 has been done for you in this question.

32.1 1930 C of electric charge liberates 0.01 mol of cobalt from cobalt nitrate. What is the charge on the cobalt ion?

32.2 0.238 g of tin can be liberated at the negative electrode during electrolysis of tin chloride when a current of 0.5 A flows for 772 s. What is the charge on the tin ion? $[A_r(Sn) = 119]$

32.3 A solution of a chromium salt is electrolysed using a current of 0.25 A flowing for 2316 s. The mass of chromium deposited on the negative electrode is 0.104 g. Calculate the charge on the chromium ion. $[A_r(Cr) = 52]$

HOW MUCH ENERGY?

◆ *TOPIC 33 ENERGY TRANSFERS IN CHEMICAL REACTIONS*

When a chemical reaction occurs, energy is usually transferred; this often results in a change in temperature. If there is a fall in temperature, the reaction is said to be **endothermic**. If there is a rise in temperature, the reaction is said to be **exothermic**.

The amount of energy released in exothermic chemical reactions can be found by transferring this energy to some water and measuring its temperature rise. In endothermic reactions, energy is transferred *from* the water, and the temperature falls.

◆ COMBUSTION REACTIONS

WORKED EXAMPLE 33A

Question

When 1.16 g of propanone, CH_3COCH_3, is burned away in a crucible, the temperature of 250 g of water in a copper can is raised from 19 °C to 41 °C. How much energy is released when one mole of propanone is burned? [Specific heat capacity of water = 4.2 J/g °C]

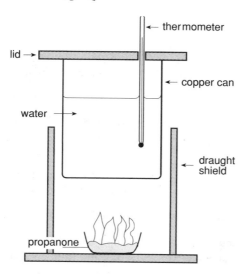

Measuring the amount of energy
released by burning propanone

Answer

You need to know about specific heat capacities (see topic 16) for step 1.

energy (J) = specific heat capacity (J/kg °C) × mass (kg) × temperature rise (°C)

Step 1	Work out how much energy is transferred to the water.	temperature rise of the water $= 41 °C - 19 °C = 22 °C$ energy transferred to the water $= 250 \text{ g} \times 22 °C \times 4.2 \text{ J/g } °C$ $= 23\ 100 \text{ J} = 23.1 \text{ kJ}$
Step 2	Work out M_r for propanone, CH_3COCH_3.	$M_r = (3 \times 12) + (6 \times 1) + (1 \times 16)$ $= 58$
Step 3	Write down the mass of 1 mol of the substance and scale down to the amount asked in the question.	$58 \text{ g} = 1 \text{ mol of propanone}$ $1.16 \text{ g} = \dfrac{1.16 \text{g}}{58 \text{g}} \times 1 \text{ mol}$ $= 0.02 \text{ mol of propanone}$
Step 4	Work out the energy transferred to 1 mol of the substance.	$0.02 \text{ mol transfers } 23.1 \text{ kJ}$ Scaling up, 1 mol transfers $\dfrac{23.1 \text{kJ}}{0.02 \text{mol}} = 1155 \text{ kJ}$

The energy released by burning propanone is 1155 kJ/mol. (The databook value is 1821 kJ/mol.)

Questions

Steps 1–3 have been done for you in this question.

33.1 When it is burned, 0.2 mol of cyclohexane, C_6H_{12}, can transfer 784 kJ of energy. How much energy can be obtained from one mole of cyclohexane?

Use steps 2 to 4 to answer these questions. [$A_r(C) = 12$, $A_r(O) = 16$, $A_r(H) = 1$]

33.2 3.6 g of butanone, $C_2H_5COCH_3$, can release an energy of 122 kJ when it is burned. How much energy can be transferred on burning one mole of butanone?

33.3 2 g of heptane, C_7H_{16}, can release 97 kJ of energy when it is burned. How much energy can be obtained on burning one mole of heptane?

Use steps 1 to 4 to answer these questions.

33.4 Using the apparatus shown in worked example 33A, 0.92 g of ethanol, C_2H_5OH, raised the temperature of 250 g of water from 20 °C to 37 °C when it was burned. How much energy would be transferred from one mole of this fuel?

33.5 The energy available when butane, C_4H_{10}, burns was found by holding a butane gas lighter underneath a can containing water. The lighter was weighed before and after the experiment. 0.29 g of butane gave a temperature rise of 10 °C in 200 g of water.

a How much energy could be transferred from one mole of butane?

b Why is this result different from the databook value of 2977 kJ/mol?

33.6 Methane and hydrogen are gaseous fuels. The energy available from burning methane is 890 kJ/mol, and that from hydrogen gas is 286 kJ/mol. (Recall that the volume of one mole of any gas at room temperature and pressure is 24 litres.)

a Which fuel transfers more energy per gram?

b Which fuel gives more energy per litre?

33.7 Natural gas is almost pure methane, CH_4. Bunsen burners that use natural gas are used for most of the heating done in school laboratories. The energy available from burning natural gas is about 840 kJ/mol. One mole of any gas at room temperature and pressure occupies 24 litres.

a How much energy is needed to raise the temperature of 500 g of water from 20 °C to its boiling point?

b How many moles of natural gas are needed to supply this energy?

c What volume of natural gas, measured at room temperature and pressure, is required?

◆ REACTIONS IN SOLUTIONS

Some reactions take place in solutions. The energy transferred by the reaction is taken from, or taken up by, the solution itself, changing its temperature.

If the solutions are dilute (and you can take this to be so for the calculations in this section), you can assume that the specific heat capacity and the density of the solution are the same as those of water, i.e. 4.2 J/g °C and 1 g/cm^3. This means that the mass of the solution is numerically equal to its volume, i.e. the mass of 1 cm^3 of a dilute solution in water is 1 g.

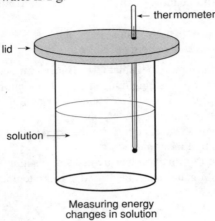

Measuring energy
changes in solution

Follow the steps of worked example 33A to answer the following questions.

Questions

33.8 When 0.4 g of calcium reacts wih 100 cm^3 (an excess) of dilute hydrochloric acid, a temperature rise of 12 °C occurs.
$$Ca(s) + 2HCl(aq) \rightarrow CaCl_2(aq) + H_2(g)$$
a Is this reaction exothermic or endothermic?
b How much energy is released when one mole of calcium reacts with hydrochloric acid?
c Explain why the question tells you that an 'excess' (too much) of the acid was used.

33.9 When 0.046 g of sodium reacts with 50 cm^3 of water, the temperature of the water rises by 1.5 °C. How much energy is released when one mole of sodium reacts with water?

33.10 When 4 g of ammonium nitrate, NH_4NO_3, dissolves in 100 cm^3 of water, the temperature falls by about 2.5 °C.
a Is this reaction exothermic or endothermic?
b How much energy is absorbed when one mole of ammonium nitrate dissolves in water?

◆ TOPIC 34 ENERGY-LEVEL DIAGRAMS

An **energy-level diagram** shows the energy transferred in a chemical reaction.

In **exothermic** reactions, energy is transferred to the surroundings. When ethanol is burned in air, the energy transferred is 1366 kJ/mol of ethanol.

$$C_2H_5OH(l) + 3O_2(g) \rightarrow 2CO_2(g) + 3H_2O(g)$$

This energy transfer is shown in the diagram below, called an energy-level diagram.

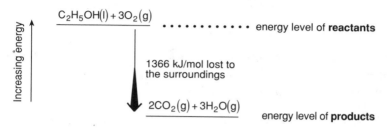

In **endothermic** reactions, energy is absorbed. The water gas reaction, in which coal reacts with steam, is an endothermic reaction. The energy absorbed is 131 kJ/mol of carbon.

$$C(s) + H_2O(g) \rightarrow CO(g) + H_2(g)$$

The energy-level diagram for this energy transfer is shown below.

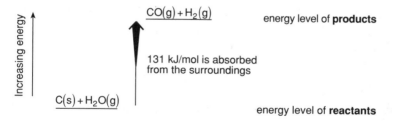

Questions

34.1 This diagram represents the energy change for a reaction.
   a Write down the equation for the reaction.
   b Underneath the equation, indicate which are the reactants and which is the product.
   c Is the reaction exothermic or endothermic?

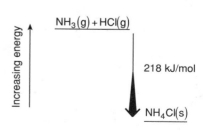

34.2 This diagram represents the energy change for a reaction.
   a Write down the equation for the reaction.
   b Is the reaction exothermic or endothermic?
   c How much energy per mole of nitrogen is absorbed from the surroundings?

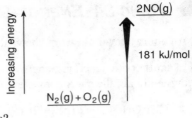

34.3 When zinc reacts with copper sulphate solution, 216 kJ/mol of energy is released. The equation for this reaction is

$$Zn(s) + Cu^{2+}(aq) \rightarrow Zn^{2+}(aq) + Cu(s)$$

Draw a clearly labelled energy-level diagram to represent this energy transfer.

34.4 When 9 g of water becomes ice, 3.0 kJ of energy is released.
   a Complete this equation for the process:

$$H_2O(l) \rightarrow \dots$$

   b How much energy is transferred per mole of water on freezing?
   c Draw a clearly labelled energy-level diagram to represent this energy transfer.

34.5 When ammonium nitrate dissolves in water, the energy absorbed by the solution is 25 kJ/mol of ammonium nitrate.

$$NH_4NO_3(s) \rightarrow NH_4NO_3(aq)$$

Draw a clearly labelled energy-level diagram to represent this energy transfer.

34.6 When 0.05 mol of magnesium reacts with hydrochloric acid, 23 kJ of energy is released.
   a Balance this equation for the reaction:

$$Mg(s) + HCl(aq) \rightarrow MgCl_2(aq) + H_2(g)$$

   b Work out the energy released per mole of magnesium.
   c Draw an energy-level diagram for this energy transfer.

Use steps 2 to 4 of worked example 33A to answer this question.

34.7 Burning 0.86 g of hexane, C_6H_{14}, in air can release 41.95 kJ of energy.
   a Balance the equation below.

$$C_6H_{14}(g) + O_2(g) \rightarrow CO_2(g) + H_2O(l)$$

   b Calculate the energy transferred on burning one mole of hexane.
   c Draw an energy-level diagram to represent this energy transfer. (Check the number of moles of hexane in the equation.)

TOPIC 35 BOND ENERGIES AND ENERGY TRANSFER

In any chemical reaction, atoms are rearranged. Bonds are broken in the substances that are reacting and new bonds are made in the products.

◆ Bond-**breaking** requires energy – it is **endothermic**.
◆ Bond-**making** releases energy – it is **exothermic**.

Each type of bond has its own **bond energy**. This is the amount of energy needed to break one mole of bonds, or released when one mole of bonds are made. Some bond energies are listed in the table on page 151.

WORKED EXAMPLE 35A

Question

Using the bond energies given in the table on page 151, calculate the energy transfer in this reaction:

$$2H_2(g) + O_2(g) \rightarrow 2H_2O(g)$$

Construct a simple bond-energy diagram to represent the energy transfers in the reaction.

Answer

Step 1	Write down the balanced equation, showing the bonds.	$2H–H + O=O \rightarrow 2\ H–O–H$

		broken	**formed**
Step 2	Write down the bonds broken and formed.	$2 \times H–H$	$4 \times O–H$
			$1 \times O=O$

		energy in	**energy out**
Step 3	Write down, in kJ/mol, the energy transfers for bond-breaking and bond-forming.	(2×436)	4×464
		$+ (1 \times 497)$	$= 1856$
		$= 1369$	

Step 4	Find the difference, in kJ/mol, between the energy taken in and the energy given out.	overall energy change $= (1856 – 1369)\ kJ = 487\ kJ$ The energy transferred in this reaction is 487 kJ/mol.
Step 5	Decide whether the reaction is exothermic or endothermic.	Energy out is greater than energy in. This is an exothermic reaction.
Step 6	Construct an energy-level diagram if asked.	See overleaf

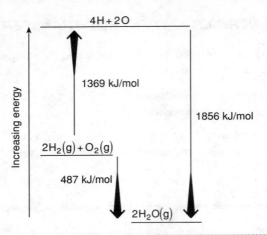

Questions

35.1 The energy-level diagram for methane burning in oxygen is shown here.

a Write down the equation for the reaction.
b How much energy is involved in bond-breaking?
c How much energy is involved in bond-making?
d What is the overall energy change in this reaction?
e Is the reaction exothermic or endothermic?

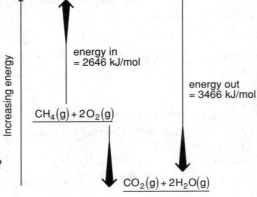

35.2 Use the bond energies given in the table on page 151 to calculate the expected energy change in each of the following reactions. Are the reactions exothermic or endothermic?

a Hydrogen burning in chlorine to give hydrogen chloride:
$H_2(g) + Cl_2(g) \rightarrow 2HCl(g)$
b Hydrogen burning in bromine to give hydrogen bromide:
$H_2(g) + Br_2(g) \rightarrow 2HBr(g)$

35.3 Calculate the expected energy transfer when one mole of methane reacts with chlorine according to the equation given below. Is the reaction exothermic or endothermic? Construct an energy-level diagram to represent these energy transfers.
$CH_4(g) + Cl_2(g) \rightarrow CH_3Cl(g) + HCl(g)$

35.4 Calculate the expected energy transfer when ethene reacts with hydrogen to form ethane. Is the reaction exothermic or endothermic?
$CH_2{=}CH_2(g) + H_2(g) \rightarrow C_2H_6(g)$

HOW FAST?

◆ TOPIC 36 RATES OF CHEMICAL REACTION

We can follow **reaction rates** by measuring how much of a reactant is used up or how much of a product is made over a given time. A fast reaction is one in which the reactants change rapidly into the products. A fast reaction has a high rate.

WORKED EXAMPLE 36A

Question

A 1 cm length of magnesium ribbon was added to 50 cm^3 of dilute hydrochloric acid. The volume of hydrogen gas produced was noted at 50 s intervals, giving the results in the table below.

Time (s)	0	50	100	150	200	250	300	350	400	450
Volume of hydrogen (cm^3)	0	32	55	68	74	78	79	79.5	80	80

a Draw a graph of the volume of hydrogen produced (vertical axis) against time.
b When is the reaction rate highest? When is it lowest?
c At what time does the reaction stop?
d Use the graph to estimate the volume of hydrogen produced after 75 s.

Answer

a

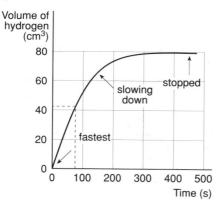

b The rate is highest at the start of the experiment, when the graph is steepest. The graph levels off during the reaction as the rate gets less, and becomes horizontal when the reaction stops.

c The reaction stops at about 400 s.

d Approximately 43 cm^3 of hydrogen are made.

Questions

36.1 The diagrams below show the apparatus used for an investigation into the effects of two different sizes of marble chips on the rate of the reaction between marble and dilute hydrochloric acid. An excess of marble was used. The results are shown on the graph below.

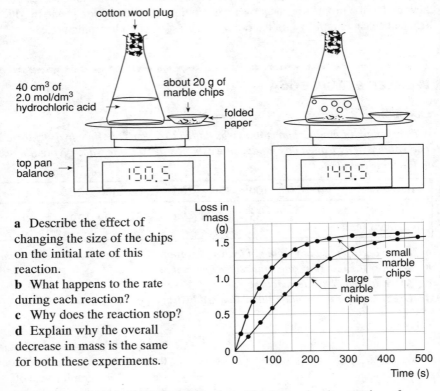

a Describe the effect of changing the size of the chips on the initial rate of this reaction.
b What happens to the rate during each reaction?
c Why does the reaction stop?
d Explain why the overall decrease in mass is the same for both these experiments.

36.2 The table shows results for the formation of hydrogen by the reaction of calcium metal with an excess of water at 20 °C.

Time(s)	0	10	20	30	40	50	60	70
Volume of hydrogen (cm³)	0	6	14	26	41	58	73	89

Time (s)	80	90	100	110	120	130	140	150
Volume of hydrogen (cm³)	102	117	131	137	140	140	141	141

a Plot the results as a graph, putting time on the horizontal axis.
b Sketch on the graph the lines you would expect if the water was kept at (i) 30 °C and (ii) 10 °C.
c Other than by raising the temperature, how else could the rate be increased?

◆ TIMING A REACTION

Another way of measuring the rate of a reaction is to measure the time taken for the reaction to reach a particular stage. It's like measuring how long it takes a sprinter to cover a fixed distance: the shorter the time taken, the faster the runner.

WORKED EXAMPLE 36B

Question

A student was investigating the effect of acid concentration on the rate of the reaction between chalk and dilute hydrochloric acid. He added the same amount of powdered chalk to three different concentrations of acid and, for each, measured the time taken to collect 10 cm^3 of carbon dioxide gas.

Experiment	Mass of chalk (g)	Acid concentration (mol/litre)	Time to collect 10 cm^3 of carbon dioxide (s)
1	0.5	2	8
2	0.5	1	16
3	0.5	0.5	32

a In which experiment was the reaction fastest?
b What is the effect of changing the acid concentration on the rate of reaction?
Answer

a Experiment 1 has the fastest initial rate because the required volume of gas was collected in the shortest time.
b As acids of higher concentration are used, the time to collect 10 cm^3 of hydrogen gets less and the rate of the reaction increases.

Questions

36.3 A student was investigating why some antacids are better than others. She timed how long it took for one tablet of each brand to disappear in 50 cm^3 of dilute hydrochloric acid. Her results are in the table below.

Brand of tablet	1	2	3	4	5
Time taken for one tablet to disappear (s)	95	163	90	155	142

a For which brand was the rate of reaction with hydrochloric acid the fastest?
b A friend criticized this experiment. He said that the tablets were different sizes and shapes, and that they could also contain different chemicals. Explain how each of these differences could affect the rate of the reaction of the tablets with acid.

36.4 In the reaction between sodium thiosulphate solution and dilute hydrochloric acid, a precipitate of sulphur is formed and the mixture becomes cloudy. In the experiment shown below, the cross on the paper cannot be seen from above once a certain amount of sulphur has been made.

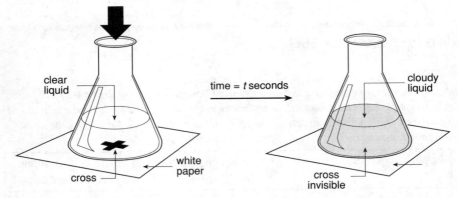

The times for the cross to go out of sight at certain solution temperatures are shown in the table below.

Temperature of mixture (°C)	20	30	40	50	60
Time for cross to be hidden, t (s)	260	130	65	31	16

a   At which temperature does the fastest reaction occur?
b   Draw a graph of the time for the cross to be hidden, t (vertical axis) against the temperature.
c   What is the effect on the time t as the temperature is raised (i) from 20 °C to 30 °C, and (ii) from 30 °C to 40 °C?

36.5 This graph shows the volume of hydrogen produced when excess zinc shavings react with 50 cm^3 of 2 mol/litre hydrochloric acid at 20 °C.

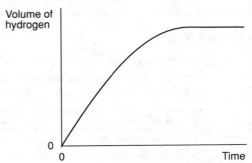

Make a copy of the graph. On the same axes, sketch the graphs you would expect if, in separate experiments,
a   the temperature were raised to 30 °C
b   50 cm^3 of 1.0 mol/litre acid were used instead of 2.0 mol/litre acid
c   a few drops of copper sulphate were added to catalyse the reaction
d   larger pieces of zinc were used.

36.6 Car bodies can be filled using 'Fastfilla'. The kit comes in three parts: the resin liquid, the filler powder and the paste hardener. The three components are mixed together and then put in the hole in the car body, where the mixture will set. A series of experiments was carried out in the laboratory to investigate the setting times of 'Fastfilla'. The results are shown in the table below.

Volume of resin used (cm^3)	Volume of filler used (cm^3)	Volume of paste used (cm^3)	Setting time
10	10	2	6 minutes
20	10	2	8 minutes
10	20	2	6 minutes
10	10	4	3 minutes
10	10	0	24 hours

a Which component – resin, filler or paste – appears to be acting as a catalyst?

b During the setting process the mixture gets warm. Why might this warming prevent these experiments being a fair test?

c The instructions for using 'Fastfilla' state that, in hot weather, it may be necessary to reduce the amount of paste hardener used. Suggest a scientific reason for this instruction.

36.7 Hydrogen peroxide solution decomposes very slowly, releasing oxygen:
$$2H_2O_2(aq) \rightarrow 2H_2O(l) + O_2(g)$$
It may be several days before sufficient oxygen is released for it to be measured. The reaction is catalysed by manganese oxide, MnO_2. The table below shows the volume of oxygen released with time when one measure of manganese oxide powder, MnO_2, is added to 50 cm^3 of hydrogen peroxide solution.

Time (s)	0	20	40	60	80	100	120	140	160	180
Volume of oxygen (cm^3)	0	10	20	26	32	35	38	39	40	40

a Draw a graph of the volume of oxygen released (vertical axis) against time. Use a vertical scale that goes up to 100 cm^3.

b On the same axes, sketch the graphs you would expect if, in separate experiments:

(i) the temperature were raised to 40 °C

(ii) 100 cm^3 of hydrogen peroxide solution were used

(iii) manganese oxide granules were used in place of powder

(iv) 50 cm^3 of a different hydrogen peroxide solution were used, which was half the concentration of the original one.

BIOLOGY

ENVIRONMENT

 ## TOPIC 37 SAMPLING ANIMALS

Capture–mark–recapture is a simple technique for estimating the population of animals in a given area. We capture a number of animals from the sample area, count them and mark them in a harmless way, and then release them; this is sample 1. After an interval of a few days we repeat the exercise, assuming that our released animals have now mixed in with the general population; this is sample 2. This time we record both the total and the number of marked animals. A simple estimate of the population is:

$$\text{Estimated population} = \frac{\text{number in sample } 1 \times \text{number in sample } 2}{\text{number of marked animals in sample } 2}$$

WORKED EXAMPLE 37A

Question

As part of her work on populations a pupil decided to find out the number of snails in the school garden. She found and marked 24 snails. A week later she discovered 21 snails, nine of which were marked. Estimate the snail population of her sample area.

Answer

Step 1   To use the equation above, we have to identify three values:

number in sample 1 = 24
number in sample 2 = 21
number of marked snails in sample 2 = 9

Step 2   Substitute values into the equation.

$$\text{Estimated population} = \frac{24 \times 21}{9} = 56$$

The estimated population of her sample area is 56 snails.

Of course, the actual population could be any number in the region of 56: it could be, say, 60 or 50. There are many variables that are not controlled and so we must consider the answer to be only an estimate.

Questions

37.1 Suggest how you might estimate the population of a particular invertebrate (e.g. woodlice) in an area of garden.

37.2 A class investigated the population of woodlice in a hedge. A sample of animals was collected on a cool, dry day. A second sample was taken during the next lesson, a week later; it had just rained.

sample	86
sample 2	74
number of marked woodlice in sample 2	4

Use these results to estimate the population of woodlice in the class's sample area. Suggest some of the possible sources of error in this estimation.

◆ TOPIC 38 TESTING PREDICTIONS

Sometimes you need to make some sort of **quantitative** prediction about your expected results. This can be very difficult in biological systems. It is possible, however, to **test** predictions against results using a simple statistical treatment of experimental data. One of the easiest statistical tests to apply is the **chi-squared (χ^2) test.** This helps us to decide just how close the actual results are to the predicted results.

Chi-squared is a statistical value calculated from the differences between expected and observed results. It is written like this:

$$\chi^2 = \sum \frac{(O-E)^2}{E}$$

where Σ means 'the sum of all',
O = observed result,
E = expected result

Standard statistical tables, like the one below, enable us to use a chi-squared value to discover how well the observed results fit the predictions.

Degrees of freedom	Number of classes	χ^2									
1	2	0.016	0.064	0.15	0.46	1.07	1.64	2.71	3.84	5.41	6.64
2	3	0.21	0.45	0.71	1.39	2.41	3.22	4.61	5.99	7.82	9.21
3	4	0.58	1.01	1.42	2.37	3.67	4.64	6.25	7.82	9.84	11.34
4	5	1.61	2.34	3.00	4.35	6.06	7.29	9.24	11.07	13.39	15.09
Probability that chance alone could produce this result		0.90	0.80	0.70	0.50	0.30	0.20	0.10	0.05	0.02	0.01
		90%	80%	70%	50%	30%	20%	10%	5%	2%	1%

The meaning of 'degrees of freedom' is discussed in the worked example.

WORKED EXAMPLE 38A

Question

Let us imagine a simple experiment with 96 woodlice in a two-option choice chamber. Side A is dark; side B is light. All other variables are controlled. The observed numbers of woodlice in the two halves are:

> *Side A (dark) 73 woodlice*
> *Side B (light) 23 woodlice*

Are these results due to chance? If not, what conclusions can you draw from this experiment?

Answer

Step 1 Write down what you know.

$$O_{dark} = 73 \text{ and } O_{light} = 23$$

In this experiment, we *might* predict that the difference in condition between the two sides would not affect the distribution of the woodlice: they might simply arrange themselves in a random manner between the two halves of the chamber. We would then expect to see 48 woodlice (half of 96) in each chamber at the end of the experiment, so the expected result would be

$$E_{dark} = 48 \text{ and } E_{light} = 48$$

Step 2 Calculate the value of χ^2.

$$\chi^2 = \sum \frac{(O - E)^2}{E}$$

Substituting into the equation,

$$\chi^2 = \frac{(73 - 48)^2}{48} + \frac{(23 - 48)^2}{48}$$

$$= \frac{(25 \times 25)^2 + (-25 \times -25)^2}{48}$$

$$= 26.0$$

Step 3 Look up your value of χ^2 in the table opposite. The 'degree of freedom' is the answer to the question, 'If the animal did not make *this* choice, how many others were open to it?' In this case, there was only one other choice or degree of freedom. If we had done a similar experiment to investigate say, damp/dry and dark/light in the same chamber, there would have been three degrees of freedom.

From the table, we can see that the probability of the observed result happening by chance alone is less than 0.01. This means that this result will occur as a result of chance alone no more than once in every 100 experiments. It seems likely, then, that a reason other than chance is the cause, and we might conclude that woodlice prefer dark conditions.

When the final probability is below 0.01 it is very easy to conclude that something other than chance must be producing the result. It is harder to conclude this if the final value is higher than 0.1. For example, suppose that the results had shown 54 woodlice in side A and 42 in side B. The value of χ^2 would then be 1.5, which gives a probability of between 0.2 and 0.3. This suggests that we could get this result about one time in four as a result of chance alone.

BIOLOGY ◆ ENVIRONMENT

Questions

38.1 A biologist was studying the behaviour of garden snails. She found a distribution in her first collection as follows:

Position	Number of snails
under stones	7
in sunlight	2
on a wall facing north	5
on a wall facing south	2

From these results she hypothesized that garden snails prefer damp, dark areas, as the greatest number of snails was found in these conditions. She also suggested that this might be because these conditions provide the greatest degree of protection from predators.

To test her hypothesis she set up a vivarium in which she could vary the conditions, using a fish tank with the bottom covered in soil.

16 snails were placed in the vivarium, and after five days the distribution of animals was as follows:

right side of the tank	8
left side of the tank	8

> A vivarium is a tank or something similar that provides a model habitat for non-aquatic animals.

First she tested the effect of darkness.

She covered the right side of the tank and left the animals for a further five days, by which time the distribution was as follows:

right side	12
left side	4

Then she tested the effect of damp. She covered both sides of the tank after spraying the inside of the right side with warm water. Again she left the vivarium, returning to take her results after a further five days.

right side	13
left side	3

Are these results due to chance? If not, what conclusions can be drawn from this experiment?

38.2 A student was investigating the behaviour of woodlice. She hypothesized that they were most likely to be found in damp, dark conditions in the presence of decaying wood. She investigated her hypothesis.

First, she set up a system to look at the importance of decaying wood. She built a vivarium and put a partition with gaps in it down the centre; the two sides were as similar as she could make them. She put 40 woodlice into the vivarium and recorded their distribution after three days:

right side	22
left side	18

Then she tested the effect of damp. She introduced decaying wood into the right side and freshly cut timber into the left side. After leaving the system a further three days, she again recorded the distribution of the animals. Her results are below.

right side	32
left side	8

Use the χ^2 test to analyse the results. Do they support her hypothesis?

38.3 As a result of this experiment, the student set up a second to investigate the effects of dampness and darkness. She built a simple four–chambered choice chamber within which the woodlice could move freely and put six woodlice in each chamber at the start of the experiment. After three hours, the distribution of woodlice was as shown. Do these results support her hypothesis?

dark and damp	light and damp
14	3
dark and dry	light and dry
6	1

38.4 A second student got a different set of results from a similar experiment: Analyse these results in the same way. To what extent do they support the hypothesis?

dark and damp	light and damp
8	6
dark and dry	light and dry
7	3

BIOLOGY ◆ ENVIRONMENT

◆ TOPIC 39 SAMPLING PLANTS

Two techniques are commonly used to produce **quantitative** estimates when sampling plants.

Transects

A transect is a line across the sample area. Every plant touching the line is recorded. However, deciding whether or not to count a particular plant can be difficult because often a plant is just to one side of the line. A more useful technique is the **belt transect**. A belt transect consists of two parallel lines drawn across the sample area; the plants *between* the lines are recorded.

Quadrat–square analysis

A square, usually 1 m by 1 m, is laid within a marked-out sample area and the distribution of species within that square is recorded. To ensure accuracy, the square is placed at random in the sample area, and a reasonable size of sample taken. In this context, knowing what is 'reasonable' is a matter of experience: 1% of the total sample area may be sufficient. We may use **density** (the average number of a particular type of plant in 1 m^2), or **percentage cover**, in which a quadrat divided into 100 smaller squares is used and we record the number of the smaller squares that contain a plant of that type.

Questions

39.1 A pupil was asked to estimate the number of daisies in a lawn. He threw sixteen 1m^2 quadrats at random in the sampling area. Here are his results:

Quadrat number	1	2	3	4	5	6	7	8	9	10	11	12	13	14	15	16
Number of daisies	7	9	4	5	8	3	7	6	5	4	8	6	5	6	7	6

a How many quadrats contained 3 daisies? ... 4 daisies? ... 5 daisies? ...
b Plot these results as a bar chart.
c Use your bar chart to estimate the density of daisies in the lawn (the average number of daisies per square metre).
d What further information do you need before you can have confidence in your results?

39.2 Estimate the percentage cover of the grass in the area shown in this diagram. Estimate the fractions for the grid squares that are partly covered by grass.

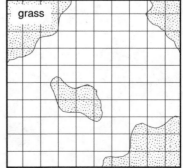

39.3 You are asked to investigate how the season has affected one of a school's hockey pitches. Give the advantages and disadvantages for this task of each of the sampling methods described above.

◆ TOPIC 40 FEEDING RELATIONSHIPS

Food chains show the flow of energy through a habitat. We start with the producer, and then show the energy flow through the consumers.

$$a \rightarrow b \rightarrow c$$

This representation shows that **b** eats **a**, and **b** is eaten by **c**. We can show this information in two further ways:

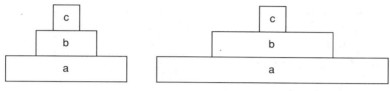

Pyramid of numbers   Pyramid of biomass

The left-hand diagram represents the **number** of organisms at each level of the chain; the right-hand one shows the **biological mass** at each level (essentially the mass of the organisms less their water content – the *living* material). The first is a pyramid of numbers and the second a pyramid of biomass.

WORKED EXAMPLE 40A

Question

Consider the following information and then sketch the food chain, the pyramid of numbers and the pyramid of biomass it describes.

Many aphids live on a single rose bush.

Ladybirds eat aphids.

Answer

rose bush → aphid → ladybird

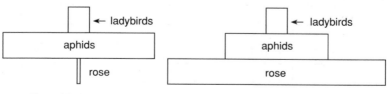

Pyramid of numbers   Pyramid of biomass

BIOLOGY ◆ ENVIRONMENT

Questions

40.1 Grass converts about 1% of the light energy falling on its surface into a form that is of use to consumers. In turn, a rabbit is about 4% efficient in converting its food into a form that any of its consumers, a fox say, can use.
a Draw the food chain represented by this information.
b If 1000 MJ of light energy falls on 1 m^2 of pasture each year, how much of that energy finds its way to the fox?
c How is energy lost from the food chain?

40.2 Growing under perfect conditions, wheat might convert 4% of the energy falling on its surface into usable foodstuffs. Should cattle farmers grow wheat to feed to their cattle?

40.3 100 people had fish and chips for lunch. It takes 1.0 kg of potatoes to make eight portions of chips, and it takes 1.3 m^2 of land to grow this quantity of potatoes (one crop per year).
a What area of land is needed to prepare 100 portions of chips?
b A cow needs 18 000 m^2 of pasture to support it for one year. How many kilograms of potatoes could be grown on this area of land?

40.4 The amount of biomass produced by a plant in a year, minus the amount used by the plant for living and growing, is called the **net production.** The table below records the approximate changes in biomass in a wood over a twelve-month cycle.

| Layer | Biomass in (kg/m^2) | | | |
	at start of year	at end of year	Increase in biomass	Percentage change
oak canopy	950	980		
shrub layer	72	80		
herbaceous layer	2.4	5.0		
fallen leaves	0.0	12.0		
roots	220	230		

a Copy and complete the table.
b Which zones had the highest and the lowest net production of biomass? Which zones had the highest and the lowest *percentage* increase?
c Explain these results, highlighting any possible sources of experimental error.

◆ TOPIC 41 CONTINUOUS AND DISCONTINUOUS VARIATION

Some features of individuals – their heights, for example – can take a whole range of values across a population: as well as 160 cm or 170 cm, for instance, people may measure **any height in between** or a range of heights either side. This is called **continuous variation.**

Other features do not show a gradual change: either you can roll your tongue or you cannot, for instance! This is usually called **discontinuous variation.**

◆ CONTINUOUS VARIATION

It is a feature of **continuous variation** that individuals' heights, for example, are distributed about a mid-point. There are three different ways of finding an average of a group of data: the **mean**, the **mode** and the **median.** These are explained in the worked example which follows.

WORKED EXAMPLE 41A

Question

A student was studying the effect of wear on the school field. He knew that dandelions grew where the grass had been badly worn. He recorded the number of dandelion plants in each of 19 quadrats that he threw randomly in his study area. Work out the mean, mode and median of the number of dandelions from his data.

Number of dandelion plants in 1 m^2	0	1	2	3	4	5	6	7	8	9
Frequency of this score (how often it occurs)	1	1	2	3	3	3	3	2	1	0

Answer

To find the **mean** in this case, we must first calculate the total number of plants found, and then divide it by the number of quadrats thrown.

Step 1   Determine the total number of plants

$$0 \times 1 = 0 \qquad\qquad 5 \times 3 = 15$$
$$1 \times 1 = 1 \qquad\qquad 6 \times 3 = 18$$
$$2 \times 2 = 4 \qquad\qquad 7 \times 2 = 14$$
$$3 \times 3 = 9 \qquad\qquad 8 \times 1 = 8$$
$$4 \times 3 = 12 \qquad\qquad 9 \times \underline{0} = \underline{0}$$
$$ \; 19 \qquad 81$$

Total number = 81 plants

Step 2   Determine the number of throws. In this case, we are told that 19 quadrats were thrown. (Check that this agrees with the sum of all the frequencies.)

Step 3   Divide the number of plants by the number of throws.

$$\frac{81}{19} = 4.3$$

So the **mean** in this case is 4.3 plants per quadrat.

The **mode** is the number that occurs the most frequently. In this case, 3, 4, 5 and 6 all occur three times and so we take the mid-point of these four values:

mode = 4.5 plants per quadrat

The **median** is the value at the middle of a list of the results written down in order of their values.

From the list in Step 1, this gives:

median = 4 plants per quadrat

Exactly which form of average we use will depend on the question and the data under analysis. If the question asks, for example, how many eggs you might expect to find in the nest of a sparrowhawk, '3 or 4' might seem a better answer than '3.9'.

Questions

41.1   The following data were gathered by ornithologists studying the nesting habits of sparrowhawks.

Size of clutch (number of eggs)	Number of nests containing this number
3	8
4	21
5	54
6	15
7	2

a How many nests were investigated?
b How many eggs were found?
c What is the mean number of eggs per nest?
d What is the median number of eggs per nest?
e What is the mode for this data?
f Draw a graph of this data, with clutch size on the horizontal axis and frequency on the vertical axis, and mark on it the mean, the median and the mode.

Work out the mean, median and mode of each set of data given in questions 41.2 to 41.4.

41.2 Clutch size of blackbirds

Size of clutch	2	3	4	5	6	7	8
Number of nests with this number of eggs	0	1	4	11	9	5	0

41.3 Number of petals on a lesser celandine (a type of buttercup)

Number of petals	5	6	7	8	9
Number of flowers with that number of petals	10	62	30	3	1

41.4 Number of dandelion plants in 1 m^2 of playing field

Number of dandelions	0	1	2	3	4	5	6	7	8
Number of quadrats with that number of plants	3	3	4	8	9	3	0	1	0

◆ DISCONTINUOUS VARIATION

Features which can show **discontinuous variation** include eye colour, height in pea plants and the inheritance of haemophilia. Pie charts and histograms are the usual way of illustrating this type of variation.

Questions

In each of questions 41.5 to 41.7, display the information as a pie chart and as a histogram. In each case, say which form of presentation shows the data more clearly.

41.5 Frequency of blood groups in a human population

Blood group	Frequency
A	41%
B	9%
AB	3%
O	47%

41.6 Frequency of eye colour in a class

Colour	Frequency
brown	35%
green	25%
hazel	15%
blue	25%

41.7 Incidence of haemophilia in Queen Victoria's children.

haemophiliac male	1
normal males	3
normal females	2
carrier females	3

… and in her grandchildren

haemophiliac males	4
normal males	5
normal females	6
carrier females	4

POOR DEAR, SHE NEVER QUITE GOT HER FIGURE BACK AFTER HER NINTH

◆ TOPIC 42 INHERITANCE OF CHARACTERISTICS

A person's appearance is due to two factors: the environment and their genetic code or genes, which are carried on **chromosomes.** Genes 'express' themselves by producing the proteins that determine such characteristics as eye colour, tongue-rolling ability, etc. Humans have 23 pairs of chromosomes, one of each pair from their father and the other from their mother. The 23rd pair determines the person's sex; they are called the **sex chromosomes.** Genes occur in pairs. Sometimes, one of a pair is more likely to express itself than the other; the one expressing itself is said to be **dominant** and the other **recessive.**

Each gene carries one **allele** out of two or more possible alleles. (Two, because the simplest arrangement is 'working' or 'not working'.) The difference between a gene and an allele is illustrated by the example below.

Gene	Alleles
eye colour	brown
	hazel
	green
	blue

We can make predictions about the inheritance of certain alleles.

WORKED EXAMPLE 42A

Question

A woman with brown eyes and a man with blue eyes have a child. The child has blue eyes. Blue eye colour is known to be recessive to brown. Use your knowledge of genetics to explain this observation.

Answer

Step 1 Define the letters to be used for each allele. Brown is the dominant allele. Let us call this allele B.

brown allele = B

Blue eye colour is recessive, and so this allele will be called b. People with blue eyes must have inherited two identical recessive alleles.

blue allele = b

Step 2 Write down the pairs of alleles being studied.

The child's father must be bb.
The child's mother could be BB or Bb.

Step 3 Show the possible crosses:

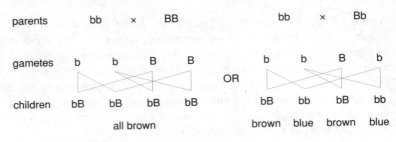

This can also be shown like this:

Female gametes	**Male gametes**	
	b	**b**
B	B	bB
B	B	bB

Female gametes	**Male gametes**	
	b	**b**
B	bB	bB
b	bb	bb

Step 4 The explanation

To get blue eyes in the next generation, both parents must be carrying an allele for 'blue', and the mother's allelles must be Bb rather than BB.

An individual carrying a mixture of alleles like this is said to be **heterozygous.** An individual carrying two identical alleles is said to be **homozygous.**

Questions

42.1 A black mouse is mated with a white mouse. All the offspring are black. Explain why the offspring were not grey. Predict the colours of the next generation of mice if the offspring from this cross were to be mated together.

42.2 A scientist's cross between a white flower and a red flower produced equal numbers of white plants and red plants in the next generation. The scientist took another red flower from the batch she used in the first cross and repeated her experiment. This time she got all red flowers. Did she make a mistake?

42.3 In humans, the sex of a child is determined by the inheritance of the sex chromosomes, X and Y. A man has one X and one Y chromosome; a woman has two X chromosomes. Explain why the number of baby boys born is roughly equal to the number of baby girls.

42.4 Haemophilia is a disease in which the blood fails to clot. Use the information about haemophilia in question 41.7 to explain how it is inherited.

42.5 A boy found that he could not roll his tongue. He discovered that, although both his grandmothers could roll their tongues, neither his mother nor his father could. Explain these observations.

42.6 Peter and Jane wanted to start a family, but both had had uncles who died at an early age from cystic fibrosis which is a disease carried by a recessive allele. What facts do you think they should be told before they can make an informed decision about whether or not to have children?

42.7 A student set up a model system to investigate the inheritance of two alleles for flower colour. He took two red and two blue marbles. The red marbles represented the dominant allele (R), the blue the recessive (B). He placed one marble of each colour into each of two paper cups to represent the alleles carried by heterozygous parents. By taking one marble at random from each cup, he simulated a breeding experiment: the two marbles represent the alleles carried by the gametes. He dipped into the cups 16 times in all, and recorded the combinations he created, e.g. RR, BR, BB and so on.

a Predict the results he might expect. Explain your prediction.

b His actual results were:

BR	RR	RB	BR	RB	BR	RR	BB
BB	BR	RB	RR	BB	BR	RB	BR

He expected that for each pair containing two blues, he would get three pairs containing at least one red. Explain why he made this prediction and suggest why it proved to be wrong.

BIOLOGY ◆ INHERITANCE AND SELECTION

◆ MUTATIONS AND CANCER

Mutations are changes in the genetic code which, in turn, change the way in which a particular gene or group of genes works. Exposure to radiation or to certain chemicals can cause mutations.

Cancer cells are normal body cells that have been altered in some way. Radiation can cause normal body cells to become cancerous, for example. Cancerous cells lose part of their growth control system and may multiply rapidly to form a **tumour.**

Questions

42.8 A scientist was studying the genetics of a bacterium. He wanted to produce a small number of mutations in his sample in order to analyse the production of an antibiotic. He exposed his sample to increasing levels of radiation and estimated the number of mutations at each level. His results are given below.

Relative radiation level (standardized units)	0	1	3	6	9	12	15	18
Relative number of mutations	0	1	2	4	8	16	32	64

a Plot this information on a graph. What does it tell you about the effect of radiation on these bacteria?
b From other work, the scientist decided that a level of about 12 mutations gave a suitable sample. At what level of radiation should he treat his samples?

42.9 A pathologist was studying a tumour removed from the throat of a human. She set up a system to monitor the rate of cell growth, using a control and an experimental culture. After one hour she added to the experimental culture a drug which she thought might help cure cancers. Her results are given below.

Time into experiment (minutes)	Number of cells in the culture (÷100)	
	No drug added	Drug added after 60 minutes
0	1	1
30	10	10
60	100	100
90	1 000	1 000
120	10 000	1 000
150	10 000	1 000
180	10 000	100
210	10 000	10

Study her results and try to explain them. You may wish to include a graph in your explanation. What other experiments might she need to do to discover the value of her new drug?

DATA ANALYSIS

◆ TOPIC 43 GRAPHS AND TABLES

During the planning stage of experiments, you should always consider how any data you collect will be displayed. You need to know the best way of displaying particular forms of data. Pie charts, block graphs (histograms) and line graphs can all help to make the patterns in your data more obvious.

WORKED EXAMPLE 43A

Question

Green plants use the energy in sunlight to convert carbon dioxide and water to sugars. The rate of photosynthesis may be measured indirectly by looking at the rate of production of oxygen.

A student set up a system to investigate the effect of light intensity on photosynthesis. He placed a few leafy pieces of Canadian pondweed in a syringe containing pond water, and held the syringe at different distances from a light source.

Distance from lamp (cm)	5	10	15	20
Volume of gas collected in 10 min. (mm^3)	118	63	25	9

a *Draw a graph of these results.*
b *Estimate the rates of photosynthesis at 10 cm and at 20 cm from the lamp. Give your answers in units of mm^3 per minute.*
c *What relationship connects distance and the rate of photosynthesis?*

Answer

a

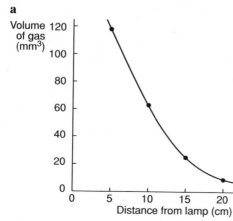

b At 10 cm from the lamp: 63 mm^3 of gas were collected in 10 minutes, so

$$\frac{63\,\text{mm}^3}{10}$$ were collected in one minute

The rate is 6.3 mm^3 per minute.

At 20 cm from the lamp: 9 mm^3 of gas were collected in 10 minutes, so

$$\frac{9\,\text{mm}^3}{10}$$ were collected in one minute

The rate is 0.9 mm^3 per minute.

c If we increase the distance from the light source to the plant, the rate of photosynthesis goes down.

BIOLOGY ◆ DATA ANALYSIS

Questions

43.1 The following table gives the results of an investigation into the relationship between the rate of photosynthesis and the relative light intensity.

Distance from light source (cm)	5	10	20	30
Number of bubbles produced per minute	14	11	6	3

    a Sketch a graph of these data.
    b What is the relationship between light intensity and the rate of photosynthesis?

43.2 Sodium hydrogencarbonate releases carbon dioxide in water. The higher the concentration of this chemical, the greater the amount of carbon dioxide available for a plant growing in the water to use in photosynthesis. A student was investigating a number of variables and their relative effects on the rate of photosynthesis. His first step was to try to discover the best concentration of sodium hydrogencarbonate solution to use in his system. Study the results below and suggest a suitable volume of solution to use in his experiments.

Sample	A	B	C	D	E
Volume of stock solution of sodium hydrogencarbonate (cm^3)	0	0.25	0.75	1.75	3.75
Volume of distilled water (cm^3)	4.00	3.75	3.25	2.25	0.25
Rate of photosynthesis (number of bubbles per minute)	27	36	45	58	65

43.3 After finding the best (or optimum) concentration of sodium hydrogencarbonate solution, the same student investigated the relationship between the rate of photosynthesis and temperature. Study the results below and explain the relationship.

Temperature (°C)	20	30	40	50	60
Number of bubbles per minute	52	129	196	80	0

43.4 A scientist studied two variables connected with the rate at which potassium was taken up by barley roots: relative sugar loss and potassium gain. Study the results from her experiment and draw some conclusions about the uptake of potassium from the soil. Try to identify a pattern in your answer.

Relative amount of oxygen	0	0.5	1.0	1.5	2.0	10
Relative sugar loss	15	20	42	45	45	48
Potassium gain	5	55	70	73	75	70

43.5 The data in the table below was collected at Rothamsted Experimental Station between 1852 and 1967. It shows the yields of grain achieved from six plots of land, each of which has received the same fertilizer treatment over that period.

Plot	Treatment	Yield of grain (tonnes/km^2)	% increase over plot 1
1	none	96	—
2	nitrogen only (N)	157	$\dfrac{157-96}{96} \times 100$
3	nitrogen and phosphates (NP)	166	
4	nitrogen, phosphates and potassium (NPK)	212	
5	farmyard manure	244	
6	NPK plus sodium and magnesium	251	

a Complete the final column of the table.
b Using the data, and what you know about the environment, suggest with reasons which treatment is the best of the alternatives.

43.6 A potometer is a device for measuring the rate of loss of water from part of a plant. It can be used to study **transpiration**, the movement of water through a plant. Water loss from a leaf is regulated by pores, called **stomata.**

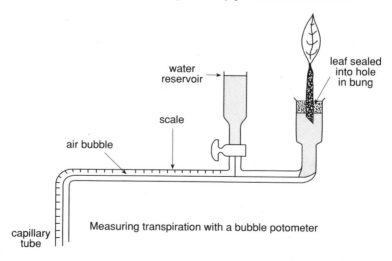

water reservoir

leaf sealed into hole in bung

scale

air bubble

capillary tube

Measuring transpiration with a bubble potometer

A student believed that the rate of water loss from a cherry leaf was controlled by two independent variables: temperature and air movements. The diagram shows a simple experiment she set up to study these variables and her results are shown overleaf. (She repeated each of three measurements five times.) Study her results and comment on her hypothesis.

Experiment	Distance moved by bubble in 10 min. (cm)				
leaf in still air	4	3.5	4.1	3.9	4.3
leaf plus electric fan (cold)	5.9	6.3	7	8.2	6.4
leaf plus electric fan (hot)	9.2	9.7	9.6	9.9	9.5

43.7 The table below shows the compositions of blood plasma, kidney filtrate and urine in a human being, in g/100 cm^3. (Hormones and other chemicals account for the remaining mass.)

Component	Plasma	Filtrate	Urine
water	90–93	97–99	96 (variable)
protein	7–9	0	0
glucose	0.1	0	0
urea	0.03	0.03	2
salts	0.72	0.72	1.5

a Explain the differences between the compositions of the three liquids.
b Estimate how much plasma is filtered to produce 100 g of urine.

43.8 Many couples use contraception to prevent fertilization. The table below gives some information about the relative effectiveness of the more common forms of contraception.

Method	Likelihood of pregnancy (%)	Improvement over no contraception
none	50	–
rhythm method	14	$\frac{50}{14} = 3.6$
diaphragm + spermicide	10	$\frac{50}{10} =$
condom + spermicide	7	
the coil and other IUDs	2	
the pill	0–1	

a Copy and complete the table.
b What other factors should be taken into account when a couple decides on a means of contraception?

43.9 Reproduction is under the control of special chemicals called **hormones.** Farmers and growers make use of plant and animal hormones to improve the efficiency of breeding, or to increase yields.
A student decided to investigate the effect of hormone rooting powder on plant cuttings. She took seven different concentrations of plant hormone and

treated five cuttings with each; she also did a control experiment, with no hormone. She recorded the presence of roots after five days and after fourteen days. (ppm stands for 'parts per million')

Hormone conc. (ppm)	Number of cuttings showing root development	
	after 5 days	after 14 days
0	1	4
10^{-6}	2	5
10^{-5}	3	5
10^{-4}	4	5
10^{-3}	1	5
10^{-2}	0	2
10^{-1}	0	1
1	0	1

a Identify three effects caused by the use of the plant hormone.
b What is the best (optimum) level of hormone to use?

43.10 In 1952, two scientists decided to discover whether there was a link between smoking and disease. They studied two groups of patients: one group had lung cancer, and the other had different diseases. The sample groups were similar in age and gender. Study the results below and suggest what conclusions the scientists might have made. Based on these data, what further studies would you suggest?

	Percentage smoking more than 15 cigarettes a day	Percentage of non-smokers
Group with lung cancer	25	0.5
Group with other diseases	13	4.5

43.11 One measure of fitness is the **recovery rate** – the time taken for the pulse-rate of an individual to return to its resting rate after exercise. Two students did step-ups onto a gymnasium bench for two minutes. Their pulse-rates were then recorded on a heart monitor for the next five minutes. Explain who is the fitter of the two.

	Sajed's pulse rate	Jon's pulse rate
at rest	60	65
immediately after exercise	145	165
after one minute's rest	85	130
after two minutes' rest	65	110
after three minutes' rest	60	90
after four minutes' rest	60	78
after five minutes' rest	60	65

ANSWERS ◆ PHYSICS

TOPIC 1 SPEED

1.1 62.5 m/s
1.2 15 s
1.3 18 000 m (18 km)
1.4 The snail. (Their speeds are 2.5 mm/s and 2.0 mm/s.)
1.5 20 s, 180 m
1.6 approximately 230 m
1.7 1.75 h (1 h 45 min)
1.8 7000 km
1.9 10 minutes
1.10 500 m/s, 1800 km/h
1.11 23.6 cm/s
1.12 **a** B   **b** C   **c** A
1.13 car A, car C
1.15 4 m/s, 12 m/s, 6 m/s
1.16 The average speed is 60 mph; the speedometer is not reliable.
1.17 13.7 km/h

TOPIC 2 ACCELERATION

2.1 4 m/s^2
2.2 10 m/s^2
2.3 0.2 m/s^2
2.4 6 m/s, 5 s
2.5 Car B. (The accelerations are 3.75 mph/s and 4.16 mph/s.)
2.6 **a** 1.6 m/s, 3.2 m/s **b** 6.4 m/s, 4.8 m/s
2.7 21 s
2.8 **a** 10 m/s   **b** 18 m/s   **c** 0.16 m/s^2
2.9 **a** F   **b** A, C and G   **c** E   **d** D
2.10 **b** 16 km/h per second   **c** 10 km/h per second   **d** 0 km/h per second
2.12 **a** 10 m/s, 20 m/s **b** 15 m/s **c** 45 m
2.13 **a** 50 m/s, 0 m/s   **b** 375 m, 500 m
2.14 **a** 3 m/s^2 **b** 96 m
2.15 **a** 5 s   **b** 20 m

TOPIC 3 FORCE, MASS AND ACCELERATION

3.1 100 N
3.2 6.25 m/s^2
3.3 500 000 N
3.4 0.5 m/s^2
3.5 0.5 N
3.6 $100\ 000 \text{ m/s}^2$
3.7 7500 N
3.8 **a** 1.5 m/s^2 **b** 3 m/s   **c** 3 m
3.9 **a** 1200 N   **b** 15 s

124

3.10 a 1 N **b** 20 N **c** 600 N **d** 5000 N **e** 30 000 N **f** 60 000 000 N **g** 0.1 N **h** 0.0005 N

3.11 a 0.1 kg, 0.16 N **b** 2 kg, 3.2 N **c** 60 kg, 96 N **d** 500 kg, 800 N **e** 3 tonnes, 4800 N **f** 6000 tonnes, 9 600 000 N **g** 10 g, 0.016 N **h** 0.05 g, 0.000 08 N

3.12 0.5 kg, 5 N

3.13 a 10 N, 2 m/s^2 **b** 20 N, 5 m/s^2 **c** 0 N, 0 m/s^2 **d** 20 N, 0.5 m/s^2

3.14 0.5 m/s^2

3.15 a 5 N **c** 10 N upwards **d** 20 m/s^2

TOPIC 4 ENERGY   PAGES 14–15

4.1 a 20 J **b** 250 J **c** 62 500 J **d** 270 000 J **e** 0.0125 J

4.2 20 m/s

4.3 a 6 J **b** 25 MJ **c** 120 J **d** 8 MJ

4.4 a 80 J **b** 80 J **c** 20 m

4.5 10 m/s

TOPIC 5 MOMENTUM   PAGES 16–18

5.1 a 2 kg m/s **b** 50 kg m/s **c** 2500 kg m/s **d** 18 000 kg/ms **e** 0.005 kg m/s

5.2 a The forward. (The momenta are 550 kg m/s and 520 kg m/s.)
b The winger. (The kinetic energies are 1375 J and 2080 J.)

5.3 1 m/s

5.4 2 m/s

5.5 15 m/s

5.6 5 m/s

TOPIC 6 WORK   PAGES 19–20

6.1 500 000 J

6.2 2 250 000 J

6.3 40 000 J

6.4 700 m

6.5 900 J

6.6 2400 J

6.7 2 760 000 J

TOPIC 7 POWER   PAGES 21–22

7.1 a 50 W **b** 500 W **c** 750 W

7.2 a 2000 J **b** 3 600 000 J **c** 72 000 J **d** 43.2 MJ

7.3 2 kW

7.4 116 W

7.5 a 200 000 J, 2000 W **b** 4000 J, 400 W **c** 4 200 000 J, 70 000 W

7.6 1500 W

7.7 20 s

TOPIC 8 EFFICIENCY

8.1

	Car	Steam train	Bicycle
Energy supplied per second	150 kJ	80 MJ	1200 J
Work done per second	45 kJ	4 MJ	960 J
Efficiency	30%	5%	80%

8.2

	Machine A	Machine B	Machine C
Energy supplied	2000 J	2000 J	4000 J
Load	550 N	25 N	1600 N
Distance moved by load	3 m	60 m	2 m
Work done on load	**1650 J**	**1500 J**	**3200 J**
Efficiency	**82.5%**	**75%**	**80%**

8.3 0.83%

8.4 60 s, 75 s

8.5 **a** 600 J   **b** 500 J   **c** 83%

8.6 37%

8.7 1.5 m

TOPIC 9 MOMENTS

9.1 **a** 6 N m clockwise   **b** 15 N m clockwise   **c** 8 N m anticlockwise

9.2 **a** 20 N   **b** 125 cm   **c** 1 N   **d** 1 m

9.3 No; clockwise

9.4 6 bricks. (Calculate the difference in their weights. How many more bricks must B have?)

9.5 5 N

TOPIC 10 WAVES

10.1 6000 m/s

10.2 hydrogen 1270 m/s, nitrogen 340 m/s, oxygen 320 m/s, chlorine 212 m/s

10.3 0.02 m, 2 cm

10.4 red 400 000 000 000 000 Hz, violet 750 000 000 000 000 Hz

10.5

Wave	Wavelength (m)	Frequency (Hz)	Speed (m/s)
water waves	100	0.05	5
sound in lead	4	325	1 300
radio (MW)	240	1 250 000	300 000 000
microwaves	0.03	10 000 000 000	300 000 000
green light in glass	0.000 000 333	600 000 000 000 000	200 000 000

10.6 **a** 6000 m/s   **b** 0.03 m (3 cm)

10.7 2.4 m/s

10.8 40 m/s

10.9 **a** trace A   **b** 12.5 Hz, 5 Hz

10.10 **a** 500 Hz   **b** 0.66 m

10.11 **a** 50 Hz   **b** one complete wave across ten divisions

TOPIC 11 RESISTANCE

11.1 960 Ω

11.2 45 V

11.3 0.025 A

11.4

Component	p.d. (V)	Current (A)	Resistance (Ω)
A	240	2.0	120
B	**3.0**	6.0	0.5
C	240	**16.0**	15
D	**2.0**	0.005	400
E	1.5	**0.015**	100

11.5 **a** $A_1 = 0.05$ A, $V_1 = 5$ V **b** $V_2 = 6$ V, $V_3 = 12$ V **c** $A_2 = 2$ A, $V_4 = 8$ V
d $A_3 = 6$ A, $A_4 = 2$ A, $A_5 = 4$ A

11.6 **a** $R_1 = 15$ Ω **b** $R_2 = 2.25$ Ω, $R_3 = 0.75$ Ω **c** $R_4 = 12$ Ω, $R_5 = 6$ Ω

11.7 30 Ω, 600 Ω

11.8 **a**

Temperature (°C)	25	40	50	65	78	89	100
Potential difference (V)	12	12	12	12	12	12	12
Current (A)	0.02	0.03	0.04	0.08	0.12	0.16	0.20
Resistance (Ω)	**600**	**400**	**300**	**150**	**100**	**75**	**60**

b See graph on right.
c The resistance goes down
as the temperature increases.

11.9 **a** B and D **b** D **c** C **d** A

11.10 30 Ω. The graph (below) is not
a straight line; the resistance
does not follow Ohm's law.

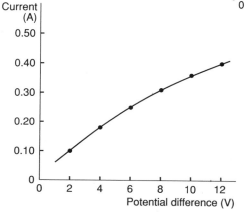

ANSWERS ◆ PHYSICS

TOPIC 12 ELECTRICAL POWER

PAGES 36–40

12.1 1200 W
12.2 3 A
12.3 6 V
12.4 3120 W, 3.12 kW
12.5 Yes – maximum normal current is 28 A
12.6 4
12.7 1000 J, 6000 J
12.8 10 hours
12.9 £1.20
12.10 24 W, 14 400 J
12.11 360 J
12.12 0.5 units (0.5 kW h), 4p
12.13 the lamp (2.4 kW h)
12.14 205 units, 1370 units; £45.58
12.15 1.2 A, 14.4 W
12.16 10 V, 50 W
12.17

Appliance	Power	Current	Potential difference	Resistance
immersion heater	3 kW	12 A	250 V	21 Ω
lamp	100 W	0.4 A	250 V	625 Ω
loudspeaker	20 W	2.0 A	10 V	5 Ω
torch bulb	1.5 W	0.6 A	2.5 V	4.17 Ω

12.18 a 30 W **b** 24 W **c** 6 W

TOPIC 13 ELECTRIC CHARGE

PAGES 41–42

13.1 0.6 A
13.2 0.1 C
13.3 1800 s (= 30 min)
13.4 12 C
13.5 32 hours
13.6 0.2 C, 12 C
13.7 160 V
13.8 1.6 A, 32 C
13.9 48 C
13.10 12 C
13.11 a 4 C **b** 1000 J **c** 250 J

TOPIC 14 DENSITY

PAGES 43–44

14.1 2700 kg/m^3
14.2 0.02 m^3 (or 20 litres)
14.3 13.6 kg

128

14.4

Object	Mass (kg)	Volume (m³)	Density (kg/m³)
W	5 000	2	**2500**
X	20 000	**5**	4000
Y	**18 000**	6	3000
Z	10 000	2	5000

14.5 Both metals have a density of 19.3 g/cm³. (Wolfram is another name for tungsten.)

14.6 120 m³, 156 kg

14.7 1.8 g/cm³

14.8 7700 g (or 7.7 kg)

14.9 40 cm³, 2 g/cm³

14.10 0.8 g/cm³ (or 800 kg/m³). (Calculate the mass of water and use it to find the volume of the bottle; then calculate the mass of ethanol and hence its density.)

14.11 10 N, 136 N

14.12 Mass of apple = 100 g; density = 0.8 g/cm³, so it will float.

TOPIC 15 PRESSURE
PAGES 45–47

15.1 greater

15.2 800 000 Pa; less

15.3 100 000 N, 20 000 N

15.4

Force (N)	Area (m²)	Pressure (Pa)
300	2	150
100 000	0.1	**1 000 000**
2 500	10	250
50	0.001	50 000

15.5 5000 Pa

15.6 0.28 N/cm², 1.75 N/cm²

15.7 5000 N/cm², 50 000 N/cm²

15.8 pressure = 500 000 Pa

15.9

Force	Area	Pressure
20 kN	40 m²	**500 Pa**
300 N	15 cm²	**20 N/cm²**
5 000 000 N	20 m²	250 kPa
11 000 kN	10 m²	100 000 Pa

15.10 300 000 N

15.11 800 000 N

15.12 45 000 000 N

ANSWERS ◆ PHYSICS

TOPIC 16 ENERGY TRANSFER

PAGES 48–49

16.1 420 000 J, 840 000 J, 210 000 J
16.2 210 000 000 J
16.3 1 540 000 J
16.4 7.5 °C
16.5 –20 °C
16.6 Both require the same.
16.7 **a** 21 000 000 J **b** 6000 s (= 100 min) **c** 80 °C
16.8 200 s (first work out the energy required, then the time); probably a serious under-estimate, since most of the energy transferred to the air will then be transferred to the walls, etc.

TOPIC 17 THE KELVIN TEMPERATURE SCALE

PAGE 50

17.1 273 K, 300 K, 473 K, 246 K, 146 K, 173 K
17.2 –273 °C, –173 °C, 0 °C, 27 °C, 48 °C
17.3 310 K is 2 degrees higher than 35 °C.
17.4 Surface temperature = 5500 °C; core temperature = 14 000 000 °C.
(The first of these is rounded off a bit; there is no point in writing 14 000 273 °C for the second, since the value given is only approximate anyway.)
17.5

Temperature	°C	K
absolute zero	**–273**	**0**
boiling point of nitrogen	**–196**	77
freezing point of pure water	**0**	**273**
boiling point of pure water	**100**	**373**
normal body temperature	37	**310**

TOPIC 18 GASES UNDER PRESSURE

PAGES 51–52

18.1 1000 cm^3
18.2 2.2 atm
18.3 1.25 ×10^6 Pa
18.4 **a** See graph on right.

b The third result is probably incorrect.

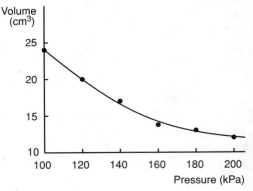

c	P (kPa)	200	180	160	140	120	100
	V (cm^3)	12	13	14	17	20	24
	P × V	2400	2340	2240	2380	2400	2400

d The temperature must have been kept constant.

TOPIC 19 PROTONS, NEUTRONS AND ELECTRONS   PAGES 53–55

19.1 **a** $^{40}_{18}Ar$ **b** $^{7}_{3}Li$

19.2

Atom		Number of protons	Number of neutrons	Number of electrons
hydrogen-1	$^{1}_{1}H$	1	0	1
helium-4	$^{4}_{2}He$	2	2	2
nitrogen-15	$^{15}_{7}N$	7	8	7
oxygen-16	$^{16}_{8}O$	8	8	8
oxygen-17	$^{17}_{8}O$	8	9	8
uranium-235	$^{235}_{92}U$	92	143	92
uranium-238	$^{238}_{92}U$	92	146	92

19.3 **a** $^{16}_{8}O$ and $^{17}_{8}O$; $^{235}_{92}U$ and $^{238}_{92}U$ **b** $^{15}_{7}N$ and $^{16}_{8}O$

19.4 10

19.5 Fe^{2+} has one more electron than Fe^{3+}.

19.6

Ion	Number of protons	Number of neutrons	Number of electrons
$^{1}_{1}H^{+}$	1	0	0
$^{35}_{17}Cl^{-}$	17	18	18
$^{37}_{17}Cl^{-}$	17	20	18
$^{40}_{20}Ca^{+}$	20	20	18

TOPIC 20 RADIOACTIVE DECAY   PAGES 56–59

20.1 **a** 10 000, 1250   **b** 17 500

20.2 **a** 1500 counts/minute, 375 counts/minute   **b** 2 half-lives = 8 days

20.3 **a** 320 counts/s   **b** 185 counts/s   **c** 55 s   **d** 25 s

20.4 approximately 3.8 hours

20.5 **a** 24 counts/s   **b** 80 s   **c** 160 s   **d** 80 s

20.6 **a** 20 counts/s   **b** 2 minutes   **c** 2.9 minutes

20.7 **a** 15 counts in 10 s   **c** 2.5 minutes

20.8 **a** 20 counts/s   **b** 2 half-lives   **c** approximately 11 400 years

20.9 54% remained; he died approximately 5300 years ago (approximately 3300 BC).

TOPIC 21 CHEMICAL FORMULAS PAGES 60–62

21.1   **a** 2   **b** 2   **c** 4   **d** 8

21.2   **a** carbon : oxygen = 1 : 2

  b sodium : sulphur = 2 : 1

  c potassium : oxygen : hydrogen = 1 : 1 : 1

  d hydrogen : sulphur : oxygen = 2 : 1 : 4

  e carbon : hydrogen : oxygen = 6 : 12 : 6 = 1 : 2 : 1

  f magnesium : oxygen : hydrogen = 1 : 2 : 2

  g aluminium : sulphur : oxygen = 2 : 3 : 12

  h nitrogen : hydrogen : sulphur : oxygen = 2 : 8 : 1 : 4

21.3   He and Ni represent atoms; CO, SO_2 and Cl_2 represent molecules; and CO_3^{2-} and Li^+ represent ions.

21.4   **a** NaI **b** Na_2S **c** MgS **d** MgI_2

21.5   **a** KCl **b** Na_2O **c** $MgBr_2$ **d** $AlCl_3$ **e** $NaOH$ **f** $ZnCO_3$ **g** $Ca(NO_3)_2$

  h Na_2SO_4 **i** $Ca(HCO_3)_2$ **j** $(NH_4)_2SO_4$ **k** Al_2O_3

TOPIC 22 BALANCING CHEMICAL EQUATIONS PAGES 63–64

22.1   Equation **a** is balanced; the others are unbalanced.

  b $2NaOH(aq) + H_2SO_4(aq) \rightarrow Na_2SO_4(aq) + 2H_2O(l)$

  c $Fe_2O_3(s) + 3CO(g) \rightarrow 2Fe(l) + 3CO_2(g)$

  d $2Li(s) + 2H_2O(l) \rightarrow 2LiOH(aq) + H_2(g)$

22.2   **a** $N_2(g)$ **b** $CH_4(g)$ **c** $Al(l)$ **d** $CO_2(s)$ **e** $H_2O(g)$ **f** $NaCl(aq)$ **g** $Ca(OH)_2(aq)$

22.3   **a** $2Mg(s) + O_2(g) \rightarrow 2MgO(s)$

  b $2H_2(g) + O_2(g) \rightarrow 2H_2O(l)$

  c $Fe(s) + 2HCl(aq) \rightarrow FeCl_2(aq) + H_2(g)$

  d $CuO(s) + 2HNO_3(aq) \rightarrow Cu(NO_3)_2(aq) + H_2O(l)$

  e $Ca(OH)_2(aq) + 2HCl(aq) \rightarrow CaCl_2(aq) + 2H_2O(l)$

  f $2KHCO_3(s) + H_2SO_4(aq) \rightarrow K_2SO_4(aq) + 2CO_2(g) + 2H_2O(l)$

  g $2Al(s) + 3Cl_2(g) \rightarrow 2AlCl_3(s)$

22.4   **a** $2Al(s) + Fe_2O_3(s) \rightarrow Al_2O_3(s) + 2Fe(s)$

  b $TiCl_4(l) + 2Mg(s) \rightarrow \mathbf{2MgCl_2(s)} + Ti(s)$

  c $C_6H_{12}O_6 + \mathbf{6O_2(g)} \rightarrow 6CO_2(g) + \mathbf{6H_2O(l)}$

22.5   **a** copper + oxygen $\rightarrow$ copper oxide

    $2Cu(s)$ + $O_2(g)$ $\rightarrow 2CuO(s)$

  b calcium oxide + water $\rightarrow$ calcium hydroxide solution

    $CaO(s)$ + $H_2O(l) \rightarrow Ca(OH)_2(aq)$

  c hydrogen peroxide $\rightarrow$ water + oxygen

    $2H_2O_2(aq)$ $\rightarrow 2H_2O(l) + O_2(g)$

  d nitrogen + hydrogen $\rightarrow$ ammonia

    $N_2(g)$ + $3H_2(g)$ $\rightarrow 2NH_3(g)$

  e iron + chlorine $\rightarrow$ iron chloride

    $2Fe(s) + 3Cl_2(g)$ $\rightarrow 2FeCl_3(s)$

f   calcium carbonate   + hydrochloric acid → calcium chloride   + carbon dioxide   + water

$$CaCO_3(s) \qquad + 2HCl(aq) \qquad → CaCl_2(aq) \qquad + CO_2(g) \qquad + H_2O(l)$$

TOPIC 23   MASSES OF ATOMS AND ELEMENTS   PAGES 65–66

23.1   magnesium (24), aluminium (27), silicon (28), phosphorus (31), sulphur (32), chlorine (35.5), argon (40)

23.2   **a** 12   **b** 24   **c** 80   **d** 137   **e** 207

23.3   **a** 2   **b** 2   **c** 8   **d** 2   **e** 4

23.4   **a** 32   **b** 18   **c** 128   **d** 170

23.5   **a** 74.5   **b** 62   **c** 267   **d** $40 + (1 + 12 + 48) \times 2 = 162$ **e** 400

TOPIC 24   MOLES OF ATOMS   PAGES 67–70

24.1   **a** 23 g   **b** 355 g   **c** 12.7 g   **d** 28 g   **e** 10 g

24.2   **a** 1 mol   **b** 0.5 mol   **c** 0.05 mol   **d** 10 mol

24.3   12 g

24.4   8 g

24.5   0.64 g

24.6   19 000 g = 19 kg

24.7   20 mol

24.8   0.1 mol

24.9   0.001 mol

24.10   **a** 71 g   **b** 36 g   **c** 128 g   **d** 31 g

24.11   **a** 97 g   **b** 165.5 g   **c** 710 g   **d** 5.35 g

24.12   **a** 0.1 mol   **b** 2 mol   **c** 0.5 mol   **d** 1 mol   **e** 0.2 mol

24.13   **a** 8 g of sulphur, S_8, contains $\dfrac{8}{8 \times 32} = 0.031\,mol$

     0.031 mol of oxygen, O_2, has a mass of 0.031×32 g = 1 g.

     b 9 g

24.14   **a** 1 mol   **b** 1 mol   **c** 4 mol   **d** 2 mol

24.15   **a** 127 g   **b** 368 g   **c** 31.5 g   **d** 0.06 g   **e** 390 g   **f** 64 g   **g** 12 g

24.16   **a** 4 mol   **b** 0.25 mol   **c** 0.25 mol   **d** 0.25 mol   **e** 1 mol   **f** 0.5 mol

TOPIC 25   FINDING AND USING FORMULAS   PAGES 71–73

25.1   **a** Mg_3N_2 **b** CH_4 **c** SiO_2 **d** $FeBr_3$

25.2 MnO_2 (manganese dioxide)

25.3 Pb_3O_4 (red lead oxide)

25.4   Black copper oxide CuO, red copper oxide Cu_2O

25.5   Sample 1 $HgCl$, sample 2 $HgCl_2$. Either their measurements are very inaccurate (if both samples were actually of the same compound) or there are two forms of mercury chloride; the latter is true.

25.6   **a** 82.35%   **b** 46.67%

25.7   **a** 88.89%   **b** 57.66%   **c** 63.49%

25.8   0.141%

ANSWERS ◆ CHEMISTRY

TOPIC 26 CALCULATIONS FROM EQUATIONS

26.1 9 g
26.2 400 g
26.3 1.6 g
26.4 1.2 tonnes
26.5 8.4 tonnes
26.6 160 g
26.7 0.56 kg
26.8 1900 kg
26.9 4.6 g
26.10 3 g
26.11 314 million tonnes

TOPIC 27 MOLES OF GASES

27.1 **a** 48 litres **b** 240 litres **c** 240 cm^3 **d** 48 cm^3 **e** 3 litres
27.2 **a** 1 mol **b** 0.002 mol **c** 10 mol **d** 0.125 mol **e** 3 mol
27.3 **a** 24 litres **b** 2400 cm^3 **c** 240 cm^3 **d** 24 cm^3

TOPIC 28 CALCULATING GAS VOLUMES

28.1 240 litres
28.2 6 litres
28.3 2400 cm^3
28.4 144 cm^3
28.5 12.5 g
28.6 **a** 24 cm^3 **b** 2 cm^3
28.7 25 cm^3 of oxygen; 50 cm^3 of nitrogen dioxide
28.8 175 cm^3 of oxygen; 100 cm^3 of carbon dioxide
28.9 Hydrogen chloride is in excess: 20 cm^3 of hydrogen chloride is left.
28.10 12.5 litres

TOPIC 29 ELECTRODE REACTIONS

29.1 **a**(i) $Na^+ + e^- \rightarrow Na$ (ii) $Cu^{2+} + 2e^- \rightarrow Cu$ (iii) $Ni^{2+} + 2e^- \rightarrow Ni$
(iv) $Fe^{3+} + 3e^- \rightarrow Fe$
b(i) 1 mol (ii) 2 mol (iii) 2 mol (iv) 3 mol
29.2 **a** 0.2 mol **b** 0.5 mol **c** 1.0 mol
29.3 **a**(i) 0.6 mol (ii) 0.3 mol (iii) 0.3 mol (iv) 0.2 mol
b(i) 13.8 g (ii) 19.2 g (iii) 17.7 g (iv) 11.2 g
29.4 **a** 2 mol **b** 0.2 mol **c** 4 mol
29.5 **a** 24 litres **b** 12 litres
29.6 **a** $Cl^- - e^- \rightarrow Cl$ **b** $Br^- - e^- \rightarrow Br$ **c** $I^- - e^- \rightarrow I$
d $2Cl^- - 2e^- \rightarrow Cl_2$ **e** $2I^- - 2e^- \rightarrow I_2$
29.7 **a** 1 mol **b** 0.2 mol **c** 0.2 mol
29.8 **a** 0.1 mol **b** 0.25 mol

134

29.9   **a** 4.8 litres   **b** 2.4 litres
29.10 **a** 25.4 g   **b** 12.7 g
29.11 **a** 0.25 mol   **b** 0.2 mol   **c** 1.2 mol
29.12 **a** 0.05 mol   **b** 0.05 × 64 g = 3.2 g

TOPIC 30 THE CHARGE NEEDED TO PRODUCE ONE MOLE   PAGE 84

30.1   **a** 0.5 mol   **b** 0.1 mol   **c** 0.02 mol   **d** 0.005 mol
30.2   **a** 0.002 mol **b** 0.01 mol
30.3   **a** 193 000 C **b** 28 950 C

TOPIC 31 ELECTROLYSIS CALCULATIONS   PAGES 85–87

31.1   **a** 0.1 mol   **b** 0.05 mol   **c** 0.033 mol
31.2   **a** 2.16 g   **b** 2.07 g   **c** 0.37 g
31.3   0.118 g
31.4   **a** 0.192 g **b** 0.192 g (i.e. same amount of Cu as is discharged at the –ve electrode)
31.5   120 cm^3
31.6   **a** 9650 C   **b** 38 600 C   **c** 289 500 C   **d** 19 300 C
31.7   **a** 19 300 s   **b** 28 950 s
31.8   772 s
31.9   0.8 A
31.10 19 300 s
31.11 0.016 A

TOPIC 32 CHARGES ON IONS   PAGE 88

32.1   2+
32.2   2+
32.3   3+

TOPIC 33 ENERGY TRANSFERS IN CHEMICAL REACTIONS

33.1   3920 kJ   PAGES 89–92
33.2   2440 kJ
33.3   4850 kJ
33.4   892.5 kJ
33.5   **a** 1680 kJ
      b The measured value is less because not all the energy from the butane is
      transferred to the water. Some is used to heat up the can and the surroundings.
33.6   **a** hydrogen **b** methane
33.7   **a** 168 kJ   **b** 0.2 mol   **c** 4800 cm^3
33.8   **a** exothermic   **b** 504 kJ
      c Excess acid ensures that there is enough acid to react with all of the calcium.
33.9   157.5 kJ
33.10 **a** endothermic   **b** 21 kJ

TOPIC 34 ENERGY-LEVEL DIAGRAMS

34.1 **a** and **b** $NH_3(g) + HCl(g) \rightarrow NH_4Cl(s)$
            reactants   product
   c exothermic

34.2 **a** $N_2(g) + O_2(g) \rightarrow 2NO(g)$ **b** endothermic **c** 181 kJ/mol

34.3

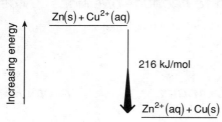

34.4 **a** $H_2O(l) \rightarrow H_2O(s)$ **b** 6 kJ/mol **c**

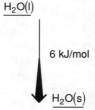

34.5

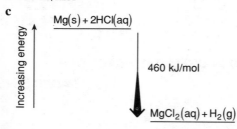

34.6 **a** $Mg(s) + 2HCl(aq) \rightarrow MgCl_2(aq) + H_2(g)$
   b 460 kJ/mol
   c

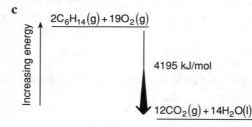

34.7 **a** $2C_6H_{14}(g) + 19O_2(g) \rightarrow 12CO_2(g) + 14H_2O(l)$
   b 4195 kJ/mol
   c

TOPIC 35 BOND ENERGIES AND ENERGY TRANSFER   PAGES 95–96

35.1 **a** $CH_4(g) + 2O_2(g) \rightarrow CO_2(g) + 2H_2O(g)$
b 2646 kJ/mol   **c** 3466 kJ/mol
d 820 kJ/mol   **e** exothermic
35.2 **a** 185 kJ/mol released; exothermic
b 103 kJ/mol released; exothermic
35.3 122 kJ/mol released; exothermic
See energy-level diagram on right.
35.4 125 kJ/mol; exothermic

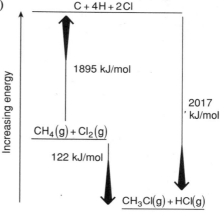

TOPIC 36 RATES OF CHEMICAL REACTION   PAGES 97–101

36.1 **a** The smaller the chips, the higher is the initial reaction rate. Particle size and surface area are related: the smaller the chips, the larger the surface area.
b As the reaction continues, it becomes slower and slower until it stops altogether.
c The reaction stops because all the acid is used up.
d The amounts of gas made in the two flasks are the same in the end because the amounts of acid used are the same. The **rates** of reaction are different but the **extent** is the same.
36.2 **a, b** See graph on right.
c Use more calcium; crush it to a fine powder.

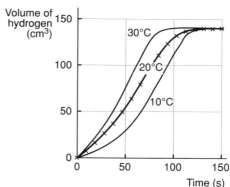

36.3 **a** Brand 3.
b The masses of the tablets could be different: those with larger mass would take longer to dissolve.
Tablets with a large surface area, even if they had the same mass, would take a shorter time to dissolve than those with a small surface area.
The different chemicals in the tablets could take different times to dissolve. In any case, the other chemicals in the pills might have nothing to do with their antacid properties, being concerned with binding the pill together and helping it to disintegrate after swallowing.

36.4 **a** 60 °C
b See graph on right.
c(i) The time taken is halved.
(ii) The time taken is halved.

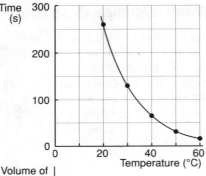

36.5 **a** The reaction rate is faster and the extent is the same.
b The initial rate is slower but the extent, i.e. the amount of product, of the reaction is about halved, because half the amount of acid is used.
c The reaction rate is faster and the extent is the same: catalysts increase the rate of a reaction but not the yield.
d The reaction rate is slower, as the surface area of larger pieces of zinc is less, but the extent is the same. Notice that in order to produce more hydrogen, more *acid* would be needed: there is already an excess of zinc.

36.6 **a** The paste speeds up the rate of setting: without paste, it takes 24 hours to set; with the same mixture and the paste, it takes only 3 minutes.
b The rate of reaction will vary with temperature, so more than one variable has been changed.
c The paste shortens the setting time, but so does an increase in temperature. In summer less paste should be used so that the mixture does not set *too* quickly.

36.7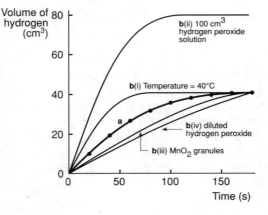

TOPIC 37 SAMPLING ANIMALS

37.1 The animals might be collected by hand, or captured in one of a range of traps. Old yogurt pots buried in the ground, or pieces of fruit or vegetable left for a few days are good ways of trapping garden invertebrates. The trapped sample should be marked and released, and then the traps used again a few days later.

37.2 $\dfrac{86 \times 74}{4} = 1591$

So we can estimate the population of woodlice at about 1600.

This technique makes the assumption that the total number of animals in the population is constant over the time between the two samples, that is, that there have been no births or deaths, and that there has been no immigration or emigration.

TOPIC 38 TESTING PREDICTIONS

38.1

Experiment	right side	left side
control	8	8
darkness	12	4
dampness	13	3

First calculate χ^2 for darkness compared with the control:

$$\chi^2 = \sum \frac{(O - E)^2}{E}$$

$$= \frac{(12 - 8)^2}{8} + \frac{(4 - 8)^2}{8} = \frac{4^2 + (-4)^2}{8}$$

$$= \frac{16 + 16}{8} = \frac{32}{8} = 4$$

From the table on page 104 we can see that there is a probability of between 2% and 5% that we would get this result through chance alone. It is highly likely, then, that this result is not due to chance but to the snails selecting the dark. Now calculate χ^2 for dampness compared with the control:

$$\chi^2 = \frac{(13 - 8)^2}{8} + \frac{(3 - 8)^2}{8}$$

$$= \frac{5^2 + (-5)^2}{8} = \frac{25 + 25}{8} = \frac{50}{8} = 6.25$$

This result is likely to happen through chance alone less than 1% of the time. It seems highly likely that the student's hypothesis was correct.

38.2 $\quad \chi^2 \ = \sum \dfrac{(O-E)^2}{E}$

$$= \frac{(32-22)^2}{22} + \frac{(8-18)^2}{18}$$

$$= \frac{10^2}{22} + \frac{(-10)^2}{18}$$

$$= 4.5 + 5.6$$

$$= 10.1$$

Looking at the table on page 104, there is a probability of less than 1% that this result was due to chance. It seems highly likely that the student's hypothesis was correct.

38.3 This is harder. We now have four options for our woodlice. If they are in one chamber, they have three degrees of freedom as to where to go. If they showed no preference, we might expect six animals in each chamber as that is how they were initially distributed, although the experiment could be improved by allowing the woodlice to distribute themselves and using that distribution to give our 'expected' values.

$$\chi^2 \ = \frac{(14-6)^2 + (3-6)^2 + (6-6)^2 + (1-6)^2}{6}$$

$$= \frac{8^2 + 3^2 + 0^2 + 5^2}{6}$$

$$= \frac{64 + 9 + 25}{6} = \frac{98}{6}$$

$$= 16.3$$

From the table on page 104, we see that, with three degrees of freedom, there is a probability of less than 1% that these results were due to chance.

38.4 $\quad \chi^2 \ = \sum \dfrac{(O-E)^2}{E}$

$$= \frac{(8-6)^2 + (6-6)^2 + (7-6)^2 + (3-6)^2}{6}$$

$$= \frac{2^2 + 0^2 + 1^2 + (-3)^2}{6}$$

$$= \frac{4 + 0 + 1 + 9}{6} = \frac{14}{6} = 2.3$$

There is a probability of between 50% and 70% that these results were due to chance. Therefore, they do not provide support for the hypothesis. The student needs to repeat her experiment several times and base any conclusions on a larger sampling.

TOPIC 39 SAMPLING PLANTS

39.1 a

Number of daisies	3	4	5	6	7	8	9
Number of quadrats	1	2	3	4	3	2	1

b

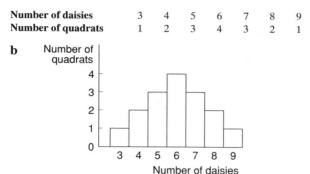

c 6 daisies per square metre

d To have confidence in the results, we need to know that the sample size was 'reasonable', and this will depend on the size of the lawn.

39.2 Approximately 25%

39.3 Visual inspection is very quick, but you do need to be able to identify a wide range of species for it to be accurate. Also, our eyes tend to be drawn towards brightly coloured flowers and this may distort the results. This method is best left to experienced ecologists.

Transects are also quick, but they measure change *along a line*. Also, if a plant is just off the line it will not be counted. A line or a belt transect is a very useful way for measuring change along a line, say between the two goals. The belt transect provides more information.

Quadrat analysis is the most revealing method, and the greater the number of quadrats thrown, the better the data collected becomes. However, it is very time-consuming. Using quadrats to measure the density of a single species can be fairly quick, however, especially if one can find a species that indicates the type of change you are examining.

TOPIC 40 FEEDING RELATIONSHIPS

40.1 a sun → grass → rabbit → fox

b The fox receives 1000 MJ × 1% × 4% = 0.4 MJ

c Energy is lost through respiration, excretion and the production of non-consumable tissues, e.g. bone and hair.

40.2 The energy converted by grass is available for as long as the grass is growing. Most of the energy converted in wheat ends up either in the indigestible stem (straw) or in the seed as starch. The costs of growing wheat are far greater than growing grass and so the farmer's inputs will be greater. He might be better off selling the wheat for flour to make bread than feeding it to the cows.

40.3 **a** 8 portions of chips require 1.3 m^2 of land, so 100 portions of chips require

$$\frac{1.3 \times 100}{8} \text{ m}^2 = 6.25 \text{ m}^2 \text{ of land}$$

b 1.3 m^2 of land produces 1 kg of potatoes per year
So 18 000 m^2 of land produces

$$\frac{1 \times 18000 \text{ kg}}{1.3} = 13\ 850 \text{ kg of potatoes}$$

40.4 **a**

Layer	Increase in biomass	Percentage change
oak canopy	30	3.2
shrub	8	11.1
herbaceous	2.6	108.3
fallen leaves	12.0	∞
roots	10.0	4.5

b Discounting the fallen leaves (since their increase was not due to *production* of biomass), the oak canopy had the highest net increase in biomass and the herbaceous layer the lowest. In terms of the *percentage* increase, though, the herbaceous layer had the highest net production and the oak canopy the lowest. The perennial plants of the canopy and the shrub layer have large masses of material remaining from season to season, whereas most of the herbaceous plants show substantial growth in a season, some completing their life cycle in one year (annuals), others in two (biennials).
c These figures are produced by estimation (you can hardly destroy an oak woodland each time you wish to investigate its production!) and so are very prone to error.

TOPIC 41 CONTINUOUS AND DISCONTINUOUS VARIATION

PAGES 111–114

41.1 **a** 100 **b** 482 **c** 4.82 **d** 5 **e** 5 **f**

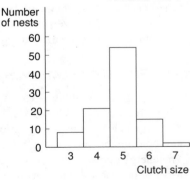

41.2 mean 5.4, median between 5 and 6, mode 5
41.3 mean 6.27, median 6, mode 6
41.4 mean 3, median 3, mode 4

41.5

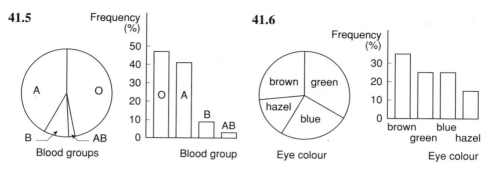

41.6

41.7 It is easier to use bar charts when comparing two or more sets of data, for example in question 41.7. In most other situations, pie charts present single sets of data well, especially when there is a reasonable difference between the values.

Queen Victoria's children

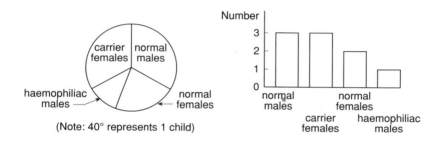

(Note: 40° represents 1 child)

Queen Victoria's grandchildren

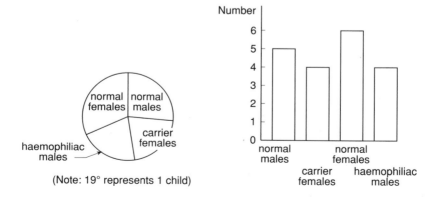

(Note: 19° represents 1 child)

TOPIC 42 INHERITANCE OF CHARACTERISTICS   PAGES 115–118

42.1 Black is the dominant allele and masks the white allele (which may in fact be a damaged 'black' allele, unable to produce the black pigment). The second generation will show an approximate ratio of three black mice to one white.

42.2 From the results of the second cross, red must be the dominant allele. In the first cross, the scientist must have selected a heterozygous red plant, and in the second a homozygous one.

Let r = white allele and R = red allele:

	First cross						Second cross			
parents		rr	×	rR			rr	×	RR	
gametes	r	r	r	R		r	r	R	R
Fl generation	rr	rR	rr	rR		rR	rR	rR	rR
	white	red	white	red			all red		

OR

42.3 If we assume that the fertilization process is random, then any egg could be fertilized by any sperm. There are equal chances of an egg being fertilized by an X–carrying sperm or a Y–carrying sperm, so the chance of producing a girl is the same as that of producing a boy.

	man	woman
parents	XY	XX
gametes	X or Y	all X
	XX	XY
	girl	boy

42.4 The haemophilia gene is carried on the X chromosome: there is no gene that corresponds to it on the Y chromosome. A female who inherits the haemophilia allele from her mother will almost always also have the dominant normal allele on the X chromosome from her father (unless he is a haemophiliac). Males who inherit the haemophilia allele will always be haemophiliac, since they cannot also have the normal allele, having only one X chromosome.

42.5 Let R be the allele for tongue rolling and r be the allele for non-rolling. The boy's grandmothers must both have been Rr, since neither of his parents could roll their tongues and so were rr. The rolling allele was not passed on to the boy's parents, and thus was not passed on to him.

42.6 Because Peter and Jane both had uncles who died from cystic fibrosis, their grandparents must have been carriers of the disease and may have passed the allele on to Peter and Jane's parents, in which case there is a chance that they will both be carriers too and might have an affected child.

Let F be the normal allele and f the cystic fibrosis allele:

Ff   ×   Ff

F   f   F   f

FF   Ff   fF   ff

FF will be normal, fF/Ff will be normal but will carry the allele, and ff will have the disease. Thus, of the four possible combinations of alleles (genotypes), three carry the cystic fibrosis allele. Since neither Peter nor Jane show the disease itself, they must be either FF or fF/Ff. If they are both FF, then all their children will be normal. If one is FF and the other fF (or Ff) then their children will appear normal, but there is an evens chance of a particular child being a carrier. If both of them are fF/Ff, then there is one in four chance that their child will have cystic fibrosis. Should the couple have one or more healthy children, it does not indicate that they are not carriers.

42.7 **a** We would predict

    RR 4   BB 4   BR 4   RR 4

as there is an equal chance of picking any ball.

b If red were the dominant allele, then any pairing containing red would show that appearance (phenotype). He based his prediction on Mendel's laws of inheritance which would give him an expected ratio of 3 red : 1 blue. However, the sample size is very small.

42.8 **a** The effect is **exponential**: as the level of radiation increases by a certain amount (three units in this case), the number of mutations increases by powers of a number, i.e. $2^3, 2^4, 2^5$, etc.

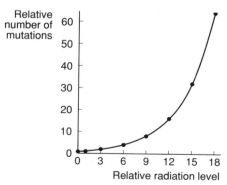

b To get about 12 mutations, he will have to use a relative level of radiation of about 10 units.

42.9 The drug does kill cancerous cells; however, it may also kill healthy cells. It also seems to act slowly, perhaps by killing cells after they have divided.

The pathologist must try the drug on normal body cells, perhaps in tissue culture, before starting trials on human patients.

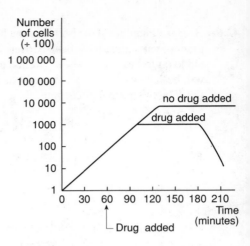

TOPIC 43 GRAPHS AND TABLES

PAGES *119–123*

43.1 a

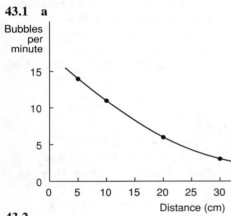

b The greater the light intensity, the higher the rate of photosynthesis as indicated by the production of bubbles. (Light intensity is proportional to $1/s^2$, where s is the distance between source and plant.)

43.2

3.0 cm^3 of stock solution provide an **optimum** rate: the curve flattens after this point, suggesting that another factor is now limiting the rate of the reaction.

43.3 This is a more complex relationship: the rate is directly proportional to the temperature over the range from 20 °C to 43 °C, after which the rate falls rapidly. The shape of this graph is typical of biological systems under the control of **enzymes**.

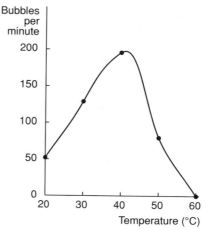

43.4

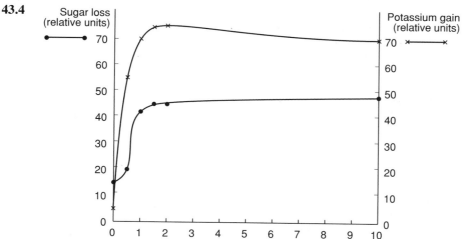

The uptake of potassium is linked to the availability of oxygen, and is proportional to it for much of the experimental range.

Oxygen is needed for **respiration**, the process in which energy is made available in the cells of living things. This experiment suggests that the uptake of potassium by roots requires energy.

43.5 **a** plot 2 64%, plot 3 73%, plot 4 121%, plot 5 154%, plot 6 161%

b Although plot 6 (NPK plus sodium and magnesium) gave the best yield, plot 5 was only just behind. Farmyard manure releases its nutrients slowly and improves the soil's structure, increasing its humus content. Also, inorganic (chemical) fertilizers are prone to leaking and tend to pollute waterways. However, to replace all inorganic fertilizers with organic ones (manure) would require thousands of tonnes of farmyard waste in addition to that which is already fully utilized. Manure is also relatively unpleasant to work with!

147

43.6 The rate of water loss is proportional to both air temperature and air movements.

43.7 **a** The kidney will receive the blood plasma minus the large proteins it contains. Essential nutrients will be reabsorbed rapidly in the kidney tubule. The amount of water and salts reabsorbed will depend on the needs of the individual. However, the levels of urea suggest that large volumes of water have been reabsorbed in the formation of urine, in which the level of urea is nearly 70 times that in the plasma.

b If 0.03 g of urea comes from 100 g of plasma then 2.0 g of urea must have

come from $\dfrac{2.0}{0.03} \times 100$ g = 6666.7 g

This implies that nearly 7 litres of blood must be filtered to produce 100 cm^3 of urine.

43.8 **a**

Method	Likelihood of pregnancy (%)	Improvement over no contraception
none	50	–
rhythm method	14	3.6
diaphragm + spermicide	10	5.0
condom + spermicide	7	7.1
the coil and other IUDs	2	25
the pill	0 – 1	50 – ∞

b Other factors to consider include age and medical history, as well as whether the methods reduce the risk of contracting a sexually transmitted disease.

43.9 **a** At high levels, the hormone inhibits root development. At lower levels, plants form roots **faster** and **more successfully**.

b

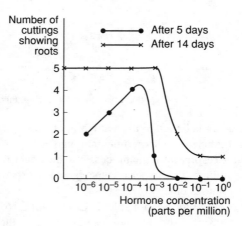

The optimum level is between 10^{-4} and 10^{-3} parts per million.

43.10 They probably concluded that smokers are much more likely to be ill than non-smokers, and that they are much more likely to suffer from lung cancer.

43.11

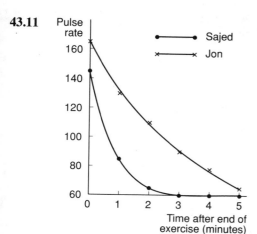

Pulse rate (y-axis: 60, 80, 100, 120, 140, 160)

Legend:
- Sajed
- Jon

Time after end of exercise (minutes) (x-axis: 0, 1, 2, 3, 4, 5)

Sajed is fitter as his recovery rate (the time for his pulse to return to normal after exercise) is lower than John's (2.9 minutes compared with 5 minutes).

REFERENCE SECTION

PROTON NUMBERS & APPROXIMATE RELATIVE ATOMIC MASSES

Element	Symbol	Proton (atomic) number	Relative atomic mass (A_r)
Aluminium	Al	13	27
Argon	Ar	18	40
Barium	Ba	56	137
Bromine	Br	35	80
Caesium	Cs	55	133
Calcium	Ca	20	40
Carbon	C	6	12
Chlorine	Cl	17	35.5
Chromium	Cr	24	52
Cobalt	Co	27	59
Copper	Cu	29	64
Fluorine	F	9	19
Germanium	Ge	32	73
Gold	Au	79	197
Helium	He	2	4
Hydrogen	H	1	1
Iodine	I	53	127
Iron	Fe	26	56
Lead	Pb	82	207
Lithium	Li	3	7
Magnesium	Mg	12	24
Manganese	Mn	25	55
Mercury	Hg	80	201
Neon	Ne	10	20
Nickel	Ni	28	59
Nitrogen	N	7	14
Oxygen	O	8	16
Phosphorus	P	15	31
Potassium	K	19	39
Rubidium	Rb	37	85
Silicon	Si	14	28
Silver	Ag	47	108
Sodium	Na	11	23
Strontium	Sr	38	88
Sulphur	S	16	32
Tin	Sn	50	119
Titanium	Ti	22	48
Zinc	Zn	30	65

NAMES AND FORMULAS OF SOME COMMON IONS

Positive ions		Negative ions	
Name	Formula	Name	Formula
Hydrogen	H^+	Chloride	Cl^-
Sodium	Na^+	Bromide	Br^-
Silver	Ag^+	Fluoride	F^-
Potassium	K^+	Iodide	I^-
Lithium	Li^+	Hydroxide	OH^-
Ammonium	NH_4^+	Nitrate	NO_3^-
Barium	Ba^{2+}	Oxide	O^{2-}
Calcium	Ca^{2+}	Sulphide	S^{2-}
Copper(II)	Cu^{2+}	Sulphate	SO_4^{2-}
Magnesium	Mg^{2+}	Carbonate	CO_3^{2-}
Zinc	Zn^{2+}	Hydrogencarbonate	HCO_3^-
Lead	Pb^{2+}		
Iron(II)	Fe^{2+}		
Iron(III)	Fe^{3+}		
Aluminium	Al^{3+}		

 # ENERGY NEEDED TO BREAK BONDS

Bond	Relative amount of energy needed (kJ/mol)
C—C	347
C=C	612
C—H	413
C—Cl	346
C—O	336
C=O	805
C—N	286
N—N	158
N=N	410
N≡N	945
H—H	436
H—N	391
H—O	464
H—Cl	432
H—Br	366
H—I	298
Cl—Cl	243
Br—Br	193
I—I	151
O=O	497